BIG CATALOGUE

BIG CATALOGUE

THE LIFE OF AARON MONTGOMERY WARD

NINA BROWN BAKER

Illustrated by Alan Moyler

New York

HARCOURT, BRACE AND COMPANY

1840 185

LIBRARY OF CONGRESS CATALOG CARD NUMBER: 56-10736

PRINTED IN THE UNITED STATES OF AMERICA

To Betty Steele

CONTENTS

1. BOY GETS JOB   3

2. CHANCE OPENS A PATH   13

3. THE BARTER STORE   20

4. MONTY TAKES CHARGE   30

5. IN THE PICNIC GROVE   38

6. ON THE ROAD   46

7. MONTY'S BIG IDEA   53

8. SUNSHINE OVER KALAMAZOO   59

9. FLAME AND SMOKE OVER CHICAGO   68

10. MONTY'S LUCK TURNS   76

11. "CONSULT OUR CATALOGUE"   86

12. THE BEST FOR ELIZABETH   96

13. THE WATCHDOG OF THE WATER FRONT   104

14. THE TWILIGHT YEARS   111

BIG CATALOGUE

1

BOY GETS JOB

It was cool and dim inside, with the sweet smell of fresh-cut wood. After the stony road, the wood shavings felt good to his bare feet. He wiped his steaming face on his shirt sleeve and took a timid step forward.

This was the first time he had been inside the barrel factory. It was bigger than it looked, with a high arched ceiling like a church. But noisy—goodness, you couldn't hear yourself think for all those shrieking band saws and clattering lathes! He wondered how the men stood it, working in all that din.

"Watch yourself, boy!" He jumped aside at the sharp command.

A bent old man was coming toward him, pushing a handcart loaded with wood scrap.

"Blockin' up the doorway," the old man grumbled. "Do better to give me a hand gettin' this stuff out to the dump."

"Yes, sir!" The boy jumped quickly, his hands reaching out to the cart. "Let me run it over to the pile for you, mister."

The old man straightened painfully and rubbed his

back. This bending and lifting was hard on old muscles.

" 'Tain't my work nohow," he muttered. "They just put it on me 'cause I'm the oldest. I may be old, but I'm the best cooper in this place, by a long shot. Takin' me off my job to push scrap around a dozen times a day—"

He rambled on while the boy wheeled the cart to the scrap pile and brought it back empty.

"Much obliged," he grunted then. "Who're you, boy? What you want around here?"

"I'm looking for a job," the boy answered. "Do you know if there's any chance for one? I don't know anything about woodworking," he admitted honestly. "But I thought I could learn."

"Oh, you thought you could learn, did you? Learn woodworking right off the bat!" The old man gave a disagreeable laugh. "Well, let me tell you, young fellow, it's not that easy. This is a skilled trade, this is. Got to know how to handle machinery, or you've lost a hand or foot before you know it. You go look for a job some place else, sonny. This ain't—"

"Eph!" An impatient voice bawled from inside. "That Number Two stock is ready now. Come on in!"

"All right, all right, I'm a-comin'." The old man started to shuffle off. Then he stopped and turned to the boy.

"Say, bub, how'd you like to be odd-job boy around here? It ain't right for a master cooper like me to be all the time stoppin' his work the way I have to. I've said so to Elder Chapin more than once. But he's pretty close. Mr. Johnny now—" His old eyes brightened. He drew the boy close and almost whispered.

"Happens Elder ain't here today. Mr. Johnny's in the office all by hisself. You go in there, sonny, and tell him you want to do odd jobs. Cartin' scrap, and sweepin' out shavin's, and fetchin' water, and the like of that. I bet they's a full day's work of it, with what me and the other fellows have to take time out for. I been doin' the most of it, and— You do that, bub. Ask Mr. Johnny for the job. You can tell him Eph recommended you. Go ahead, now. The office is right in there."

He gave the boy an encouraging push. The office was a partitioned space at the far side of the great room. A young man sat at the roll-top desk busily writing in a ledger.

The boy had time to feel glad that it was Mr. Johnny rather than Elder Chapin. He had seen the Elder passing the plate in church, an awesome figure in his frock coat and long white beard. John Jones, his partner, was a young man admired by the town boys for the fast horses he drove. He looked up now with an encouraging smile.

"Hello, sonny. Something you wanted?"

"I—I wondered if you could use an odd-job boy, Mr. Jones. I'm a hard worker, and I'm strong as a man, almost. I could pick up scrap, and handle lumber, and— well, do odd jobs. Mr. Eph said you needed someone for that. He said to tell you he recommended me."

"I bet he did!" The young man laughed. "Well, it's not a bad idea. How old are you? And whose boy are you?"

"I'm fourteen, Mr. Jones, but you can see I'm big for my age. My pa is Sylvester Ward. I don't expect you know him. He clerks at Edzell's hardware store."

"No, I don't think—wait a minute! Isn't Ward the Jersey fellow who got stung with the Beehive Emporium? Put all his money into it, and when he got here, he found the rascal had moved out the stock and left town? I was east at college when it happened, so I never did hear the whole story. But it seems to be the town joke."

The boy flushed. "It wasn't much of a joke to my folks, Mr. Jones. Pa put every cent he could scrape up into that store. Sold his farm back at Chatham, New Jersey, and moved his family here to go into business. The advertisement made it look so good! He thought we'd get rich out here."

Jones nodded. "A lot of people back East think they can make their fortunes in Michigan, sonny. Your father isn't the first to be swindled, and he won't be the last. But he shouldn't have been so trusting."

"I know that, Mr. Jones. My pa is an awful trusting man. He wouldn't cheat anybody, and he never thinks anybody might cheat him. Maybe that's why he don't get ahead faster. I don't know." The boy sighed. "He works so hard, and he's trying to save up enough money to start the store with his own stock. But seems like something is always coming along to spend it on. That's why I want to get a job. If I can earn a little, it'll help some."

"Your father still expects to run the Beehive as a store, then? I hadn't heard that."

"He's been expecting to for a good six years now," the boy said ruefully. "I don't know if it'll ever happen. My mother's got so she don't care so much. She says a pay check coming in every week is better than taking chances on trade. But Pa is all for the store. Anyway, my folks make out all right. It's just that a little extra money would be welcome. So if you could see your way to giving me that job—"

"I'm thinking about it, boy. Would you want it just for school vacation or all the time?"

"Oh, all the time," the boy said positively. "I'm fourteen; that's old enough to quit school. It's time I started to take some of the load off Pa's shoulders. So if you could just give me a chance—"

Mr. Johnny smiled his friendly smile. "I can, and I will. There won't be much money in it, though. I could only offer you twenty-five cents a day for the kind of work you could do."

"Oh, that's fine," the boy said eagerly. "I could buy my own clothes on that and maybe help a little with the girls' shoes. It costs an awful lot to keep us all in shoes, Mr. Jones."

"I can imagine. Well, then—what's your name, now?"

"Aaron Montgomery Ward, only nobody ever uses the 'Aaron.' My folks just call me Monty."

"All right, Monty. You're hired. Go tell your friend Eph I said to put you to work. If I know the old man, he'll find plenty to keep you busy."

Darkness was falling as he hurried home. Home was not a house but a store building at the far end of Main Street.

It was a big barn of a place, with a false front that made it look as though it had a second floor. Ma had made her husband take down the sign. She had curtained the show windows solidly in turkey-red calico. But nothing could make it look like a dwelling house. The Wards didn't keep a store. They lived in one.

It was an old story now. But, as Mr. Johnny had said, it was still the town joke. The Beehive had always been an unlucky store. Several merchants had gone broke there. It had stood empty for years before a stranger from Detroit bought it for almost nothing. He stocked it with flashy merchandise but never opened for business. Instead, he advertised it for sale in an Eastern farm paper.

The advertisement appealed to Monty's father, Sylvester Ward. Mr. Ward was a New Jersey farmer who had always wanted to keep store. He also wanted to go west. All around him, Jersey farmers were loading their covered wagons and striking out for Michigan or Indiana.

The Wards were already talking about Michigan when the advertisement fell into Pa Ward's hands.

It was most alluring. A well-stocked general store in a booming town on the St. Joseph River—complete with a fine line of dry goods, kitchenware, shoes, and notions. The chance of a lifetime!

Mr. Ward wrote to inquire and got a series of glowing letters. Monty could remember the discussions when each one came. Certainly this was the chance of a lifetime, the opportunity that might never come again. With his wife's full approval, Mr. Ward put up his farm for sale. The money was sent off to Michigan and the deal concluded.

It was an exciting journey. Late in the autumn of 1852, the Wards said good-by to their old home near Chatham, New Jersey. Monty, born February 17, 1844, was eight years old. The family traveled by steamer up the Hudson River and then along the Erie Canal to Detroit. There Pa Ward hired a lumber wagon and team to take them overland to Niles.

Young Monty winced now as he recalled that bleak arrival. The Beehive Emporium was there, but the fine line of merchandise was not. The place was dark and cold and empty, with not even a candle left to light the rough bare counters.

The neighbors were amused but kind. They took the forlorn little family in for the night. A job was found for Mr. Ward. There was angry talk of suing the Detroit gentleman, if he could be found. He was never found.

He had left no address when he left the hotel where he had lodged for a few weeks. No doubt he was off to work his bunco game in some new community.

The family moved into the store. They had to have a roof over their heads, and this at least was their own. Mrs. Ward did what she could to make it homelike. At the worst, she said cheerfully, it was better than a pioneer log cabin. Her children did not find it a bad place at all.

Now, as Monty approached, the front was dark and the big door nailed shut as always. Pa Ward had firmly refused to make any changes in the front, which was the showroom part. The shelves were still in place, waiting for the day when he could fill them with new wares.

Monty went around to the back, where the family lived. The old stock room was now combination kitchen and living room, with sleeping quarters opening out of it. The family was gathered around the supper table.

The boy strode up to the table and spun a silver quarter on it.

"My first day's pay!" he announced proudly. "I got me a job, Pa."

"You did?" Mr. Ward beamed. He was a gentle, cheerful little man, always ready to look on the bright side. "Well, good for you, son! You make me proud of you."

Mrs. Ward was more cautious.

"Is it a steady job, Monty?" she asked. "Will they want you back again? Or was it just for today?"

"It's for every day, Ma. At the Jones & Chapin barrel factory. Mr. Johnny Jones hired me. He's an awful fine man, I think. Don't put on any airs. Talked to me just like I was a friend of his."

"Well, pull up your chair and eat while you tell us about it."

Mrs. Ward filled his plate from the stove; boiled pork and greens and white beans, with a helping of mixed pickles. The boy ate with keen appetite, trying to answer questions at the same time.

His two older sisters soon left the table. They were going to a taffy pull and had no time to listen to their brother's adventures. But Brudge, the younger boy, and the three little girls were greatly impressed.

"What are you going to do with all your money, Monty?" the little boy asked.

"That's for Ma to say." Monty smiled at his mother, busy clearing the table. "Here you are, Ma. I guess you can find a good use for it."

"I guess I can," she admitted. She patted his rough dark hair tenderly. "I declare, I hate to take it from you, Monty."

"Oh, that's all right," he said happily. "Plenty more where that came from! You got another workingman in the family now, Ma, so don't stint yourself when you go to the store."

2

CHANCE OPENS A PATH

Monty put in nearly a year as odd-job boy at the barrel factory. He left it for a better job in a brickyard also owned by Jones and Chapin.

The job was better because it paid more. He worked a fourteen-hour day, six days a week, loading brick on scows for shipment down the river. His wage was a dazzling half-dollar every single day. No skill or training was required; only strong muscles and a willingness to obey orders. It was hard, exhausting work, and it led nowhere. Monty might have spent his life as a day laborer. He had two years of it before chance opened a new path for his feet.

One of the brickyard customers was Captain Boughton, who owned the brick-carrying scows. Captain Boughton owned other boats on the river, too, and even a steamer that traveled regularly across Lake Michigan to Chicago. In St. Joseph, the harbor town where river and lake met, Captain Boughton had other business interests.

The Captain came ashore looking for Elder Chapin one day and did not find him. The foreman at the brickyard said the boss was in St. Joe for the day. The Captain swore a mighty oath and stalked back to the dock. His temper was not helped by the fact that he found his boat deserted.

He turned back to the pier, empty except for a boy stacking bricks.

"Where'd they go?" the Captain barked. "Did you see anything of my crew, son?"

Monty straightened up. "Yes, sir. I heard them talking among themselves. They said you'd be here at least an hour, and they'd have time to go into town."

"Straight to the nearest tavern, I'll bet," the Captain said grimly. "Well, I'm not going to run after them in this sun. They'll hear from me when they get back."

He lowered himself to a convenient beam and mopped his face. The Captain was a fat man, and the Michigan sun was fierce.

"Would you like a drink, sir?" Monty asked shyly. "I've got a fresh bucket of spring water here. It's not had time to get warm yet."

"Bring me a dipperful." The Captain drank deep and looked a little milder. "Thank'ee, young feller. One of Elder's men, be you? How do you like your job?"

Monty set the pail down and went back to piling bricks. No one had ever asked him how he liked his job. It paid him three dollars a week—fine wages for a seventeen-year-old boy. He was supposed to like it. It gave him a guilty feeling to admit even to himself that he hated it.

"Well?" the Captain demanded. "You don't like it—

is that it? Speak out, boy. Elder Chapin ride you too hard?"

"Oh, no, sir." Monty looked up. "The Elder won't stand for any loafing, but he's a good boss. I get along with him fine. It's just—oh, nothing. The job's all right."

He went on with his work, and there was a long silence. Captain Boughton filled and lighted his pipe. Then he spoke quietly.

"Time I was about your age, my old man apprenticed me to a shoemaker. That was back in New Bedford, Massachusetts, where the whaling ships go out. Shop was right down by the harbor, where I could see the sails. It nigh drove me crazy, sitting all day at a bench, watching them sails move out to sea."

He smoked thoughtfully for a minute and then grinned. "Well, I up and run away to sea one fine day, that's what I done. Never regretted it, neither. Fellow's got to work, same as a horse has. But a horse don't get no choice. A man's not a horse. He's got a right to choose his work. And it ought to be something he can put his heart into—something he can think about, and plan for, and make something out of. A man ought to be able to put his whole heart into his work—not just his back, like you're doing with them bricks."

Monty did not answer. He dared not. Just such thoughts as this had come to him, plodding home after a long day's toil. What's it all for? Where am I getting? Is this all there is to life?

He had put the wicked thoughts away, ashamed that they came into his mind. It was sinful to hate work. Everybody knew that. But it wasn't work itself that he hated. He knew that now, listening to this queer old man. There could be another kind of work you wouldn't hate. If only you could find that kind!

He glanced sideways at the old man's face. It was a peaceful, contented face now, as the Captain smoked and looked out at the river. *Did* he dare? The Captain himself had left a hateful job and found the right one. Surely, surely he would understand!

Keeping his hands and eyes busy with the bricks, Monty

said in a low voice, "I don't like this job very much. Could you tell me how to get one that—that I could put my heart into, like you said?"

"Well, now, maybe I can," the Captain said heartily. "What would you like to do if you could pick and choose? Like to be a sailor?"

"Maybe," Monty said doubtfully. "But you said it ought to be something I could think about—use my head, sort of. A sailor doesn't do much of that, does he? Unless he gets to be a captain, of course," he added hastily.

The Captain chuckled. "Well, I'm not hiring any deck hands right now, anyway. But I tell you where I do need a boy. That's in my store in St. Joe. You use your head in storekeeping all right. Don't know if you'd be any good at it. But it'd give you a chance to find out."

"I know I'd like storekeeping!" Monty said eagerly. "Would you try me, Captain?"

"Well, you'd have to start pretty low on the ladder, boy. Sweep out, open cases, keep up fires, and carry out ashes—that kind of thing. When there was a rush, you could try your hand at waiting on the kids. Might take you a year or two to work up to a clerk's job. Maybe longer. And of course you mightn't be any good. Then I'd fire you, naturally."

"Naturally," Monty agreed. "I don't know whether I'd be any good or not. I wouldn't expect you to keep me if I wasn't. But I'd try my best, Captain."

The Captain studied the earnest young face. "Somehow, I think you'd make out all right, son. Now I tell you. I'd pay you $5.00 a month and keep for the first few months, while we found out what you could do. That suit you?"

The glow died from Monty's eyes. "I'm making $12.00 here," he said slowly.

"And what'll you be making five years from now?" the Captain demanded. "Or thirty years, if your back holds out? The same old twelve dollars! But suit yourself, boy. Suit yourself. Only don't go around saying you didn't have any choice in the work you do. I've offered you one. Take it or leave it."

"I wish I could take it," Monty said wistfully. "But you see, I help my folks a little out of what I earn. If I just had myself to think of, I'd jump at it. But as it is—"

"Well, you talk to your pa. You get your keep with me, remember—that means one mouth less for him to feed at home. See what he says. You can let me know the next time I come upriver. There come them rascals now!"

He stormed off to hustle his crew aboard. Long after the boat had disappeared down the river, Monty worked with his brain in a whirl. He was giving his mother $1.50 out of his weekly $3.00. Did what he ate cost that, or more, or less? He had no idea. I do eat an awful lot, he thought hopefully. Maybe it'd be a saving, having me gone. And I'd have the $5.00 clear, so I could still send home something.

He put it up to his parents that night. To his relief, they thought well of the plan.

"I've always thought that brickyard work was too hard for you," Ma said. "You'd have it a heap easier in a store. I think you ought to take it, Monty."

"But how about the money?" he asked anxiously.

"Don't you worry about the money," his father put in. "It's different from when you got your first job. Then we needed every penny to keep us going. But now, with your two sisters getting married pretty soon, and Brudge working out at the peach orchard— Well, looks like we're past the pinch. You done your part getting us past it, son, and more. Now you got a right to think about what's best for yourself. If you want Cap Boughton's job, you take it. I know if it was me, I'd jump at it."

One week later, Monty was waiting on the pier when Captain Boughton's boat came upstream.

"If that job's still open, Captain," he said eagerly, "I want it! I talked to my folks, and they say to go ahead. I can start anytime you say, so long as I give Elder Chapin notice."

The Captain laughed. "And I bet you can't wait to do that, sonny. This time next week suit you? Then you be down here with your carpetbag, and we'll pick you up."

3

THE BARTER STORE

St. Joseph, Michigan, was a flourishing lake port, considerably larger than Monty's home town of Niles. Its twin village, Benton Harbor, was a woodworking center, but St. Joseph lived on shipping.

From its harbor the long ships plied across the lake to Chicago and Milwaukee loaded with Michigan lumber and grain—and, at this time of the year, with Michigan peaches.

Peaches were nothing new to young Ward. All the farmers around Niles relied upon fruit as their principal crop. Most of the barrels turned out at Mr. Johnny's factory were peach barrels. But Monty had never seen peaches in such quantities as came to the St. Joe docks. Day and night, in this summer weather, the air was heavy with the rich, tantalizing smell.

There was no refrigeration, and the shippers had to work fast before the precious cargo spoiled. Flares burned on the dock all night long. Captain Boughton was everywhere, urging the loaders to greater speed. While the peach season lasted, he had no time to spare for his store.

The store, Monty discovered, was rather an odd one. It

was a big shabby warehouse near the river. No attempt was made to attract town trade. Captain Boughton's customers were the farmers who brought their products to town. The business done there was one of barter. So many bushels of peaches for a suit of clothes; so much corn for shoes or a dress length of flannel.

This business of barter was common enough in all country villages. Larger towns, such as St. Joseph, rather looked down upon it. Farmers with produce to trade found themselves more comfortable in Captain Boughton's place than in the more citified shops on Main Street.

The Captain dropped Monty off at the dock on a bright July morning. The big steamer was waiting for the load his smaller boat had brought.

"There she is." Captain Boughton gestured toward the store. "Won't have time to take you over. Just go along and tell Carver I sent you. He'll put you to work."

Monty picked up his carpetbag and made his way to the store. Several loaded wagons stood at the hitching rail. Inside, the single big room was already filling up with farmers and their families.

To the boy in the doorway, the scene was one of complete confusion. There were no counters, no shelves. Big wooden packing boxes spilled their contents onto the floor. Side by side with the store's goods were the barrels and crates of produce the farmers had brought in. The floor was littered with excelsior packing, with overripe peaches trampled underfoot, with stray cabbage leaves and corn husks. A coop full of live chickens squawked furiously above the din of human voices.

Monty waited a minute, trying to sort it all out. Near him a calico-clad farm woman was trying on shoes. There was no place for her to sit down. She stood on one foot, balancing herself with the aid of a woman clerk, while a little girl tugged at her skirts. Further along, an old man was unrolling a length of oilcloth for two women. Farm families were milling about, picking up articles and laying them down, waiting for someone to attend to them.

Monty picked his way toward the back, where a young man was arguing violently with a farmer and his half-grown son. The young man would be Mr. Carver, the manager, he decided. He drew close and listened.

It was all about a load of green corn the farmer had in his wagon outside. Mr. Carver had inspected the corn. He had agreed that it was worth a suit of clothes for the boy. Here was the suit. All right, maybe it wasn't the finest quality cloth. What could you expect for one measly load of roasting ears? So the boy wasn't satisfied with the fit or the color, was he? Now that was just too bad. It was news to Mr. Carver that a farm kid had to dress like a gentleman going to the governor's ball. This was plenty good enough for country wear. No, he couldn't offer any other suit. Not for that corn. Take it or leave it.

Grumbling, the farmer took it. As soon as they left, Monty approached the manager.

"I'm the new boy," he said awkwardly. "Captain Boughton said you'd put me to work."

"I'll do that all right," Mr. Carver snapped. "No loafing around here, as you'll find out. What's your name? Ward? Come along, Ward."

He led the way to a door in the rear. Beyond it was a storeroom cluttered with packing boxes.

"Open these up," the manager ordered. "Get the stock out and fill up the boxes inside. Shoes with the shoes, yard goods on top of yard goods. You understand? Don't let 'em get low. As soon as one of these boxes is empty, split it up for kindling and pile it in the woodshed outside.

"You'll bunk there." Carver pointed to a cot in the corner. A packing box beside it held a tin washbasin and pail. "Miss Mattie will show you where to put the stuff inside. Step lively, now."

Miss Mattie was the clerk who had been selling shoes. She smiled at Monty as he approached her with an armload of rubbers and gum boots.

"Women's and children's in this box; men's in that one. Here, I'll help you. I like to keep 'em sorted out, though Mr. Carver thinks that's just my fussiness. Well, so you're our new mealer. Didn't Captain tell you? He wants you to sleep in the store, sort of a guard against thieves. But you're to have your meals at my house. Hope we can fill you up—I know you boys all have hollow legs."

She chattered on while they worked, demanding to know his name, how many brothers and sisters he had, and whether he smoked or drank or chewed tobacco.

"Because I might as well tell you now," she said severely, "Mother won't have any of that around her house. She's mighty strict."

Monty grinned. "So's my ma. I've never touched liquor or tobacco, ma'am. She'd make Pa lick me if I did. She only lets him smoke his pipe out in the woodshed."

Miss Mattie nodded approval. "I knew you came from a good home, minute I set eyes on you. But I had to ask. There. Now you better look around and see what else is getting low and fill up where it's needed."

The store, which had opened at daybreak, closed for an hour at noon. Monty went home with Miss Mattie Diefendorf for midday dinner.

The tiny frame cottage was almost smothered in a blaze of blooming petunias. Stiff white lace curtains draped the windows. Mrs. Diefendorf met them at the open door. Like her spinster daughter, she was plump and rosy and cheerful.

"This is Monty Ward, Mother," Miss Mattie said. "He comes from Niles City, and he's going on eighteen, and he's got no bad habits. He was raised Evangelical, but he'd just as lief go to the Baptist church with us, only I can't coax him to sing in the choir. And—well, I guess that's all I've found out about him so far."

The older woman smiled. "You'll find out all there is

to know, I guess. Looks like I'll never break you of asking personal questions, daughter. Come in, Monty. I declare, it'll be good to have a man to cook for. Since my husband passed on, I don't seem to have the heart to do much for just two women."

In the tidy dining room, Monty pulled up his chair and looked in amazement at the loaded table.

The red-checkered cloth was scarcely visible below the platter of fried chicken and the huge vegetable dishes of new potatoes, green peas, beans, young carrots, and cabbage. There were half a dozen glass dishes of pickles and jellies, and a magnificent blackberry pie.

Mrs. Diefendorf bustled out to the kitchen and came back with a plate of oven-hot buttermilk biscuits.

"Coffee or tea?" she asked. "I made both. Mattie and me mostly take tea, but Mr. Diefendorf was a great hand for his coffee."

"I'll have tea, please," Monty answered. "We only have coffee at breakfast at our house. Ma says it's too expensive for every meal."

Mrs. Diefendorf nodded sympathetically. Had to watch the pennies at his house, did they? She'd guessed as much. The boy hadn't been able to hide his astonishment when he caught sight of her table. Probably looked like a Thanksgiving Day feast to him. No wonder he was so lean through the ribs. Needed feeding up, he did. Well, he'd come to the right place for it.

The two women watched with pleasure as Monty ate

his way through the mammoth meal. Spurred by his example, they ate heartily themselves.

"I declare, there's nothing like the sight of a good appetite to give *me* an appetite," Miss Mattie remarked. "Don't know when you've had better luck with your biscuits, Mother."

"I thought they were a mite heavy," her mother protested. "And the pie crust could have been flakier. But the chicken was done to a turn, if I do say it. Not that I want to brag on my own cooking."

"But you've got a right to brag, Mrs. Diefendorf," Monty said sincerely. "When anybody can cook like that, it's—well, it's just a wonder, that's all! I guess you win all the prizes at the county fair, don't you?"

"Well, I've won my share," the widow admitted. "How about another piece of pie, now?"

Miss Mattie glanced at the clock. "He won't have time, Mother. Wouldn't do for him to be late his first day. Mr. Eagle-Eye Carver will be on the watch. Come on, Monty. We better make tracks."

Mr. Carver kept Monty busy until the store closed at sundown. He unloaded peaches and garden produce taken in trade and trundled them down to the pier for shipment. He carried heavy bundles to the wagons and fed and watered the customers' horses. When the store closed, he swept out and covered the stock for the night. Then he went home with Miss Mattie for another lordly meal.

"Carver's satisfied with you," Miss Mattie told him as

they walked along. "He don't say much, but you could see. He likes the way you hop to it the first time he speaks. Looks like you got yourself a steady job, sonny."

"I hope so," Monty answered. "I like the work. But Miss Mattie, does the store have to be such a mess? I mean—well, wouldn't it be better if there was some sort of system to it—like the stock all on one side, where it wouldn't get mixed up with the farm stuff? I don't mean to find fault," he added hastily.

The little woman nodded. "That's exactly what I've told the Captain myself. He just laughs, and says he leaves the store to Carver. And Carver don't care. All he's interested in is to bargain the farmers down as low as he can. He says that's what he's there for."

"Yes, but—" Monty hesitated, and then plunged ahead. "He's so hateful to the farmers! Talks to 'em like they were the dirt under his feet. You'd think he could be a little polite."

"Carver would say you don't waste politeness on hayseeds, Monty. He's a town man, and all town folks feel like they're better than country people. You'll find it in all the stores here in St. Joe. Everybody looks down on the rubes, as they call them."

"You don't, Miss Mattie. I noticed how nice you are to the farm women and the kids."

"Oh, I'm just a rube myself," she said cheerfully. "I was born on a farm. My folks didn't move to town till I was a big girl. So to me farmers are just as good as anybody else. But most of the folks in St. Joe don't feel that way."

"Why, of course farmers are just as good as anybody else!" Monty said indignantly. "And they got a right to be treated as good, too. If *I* had Mr. Carver's job——"

Miss Mattie laughed. "Who knows? Maybe you'll have it one day. Young Mr. Carver's not going to be with us forever. He's saving his money to open a store of his own. Old Man Brown is too feeble to take his job. Maybe it'll fall to you."

"Well, if it ever does," Monty said seriously, "that'll be a different store back there. And it'll be run a lot different from what it is now."

MONTY TAKES CHARGE

It was less than six months later that young Mr. Carver departed to open his own store. As his successor, Captain Boughton named Mr. Brown. This was the old gentleman who had been Miss Mattie's fellow clerk.

"I know he's deaf and not very spry," the Captain told Miss Mattie and Monty. "But he's been with me a long time, and I hate to pass him over. You two will have to help him out. Monty, I'm hiring a new boy and moving you up to clerk in Brown's place. Just make out the best you can."

They made out very well. Old Man Brown, proud of his new title, was quite content to leave his new duties to his staff. Between them, Miss Mattie and Monty ran the store. They ran it with an efficiency unknown up to now.

Their first move was to separate the two departments. One side of the store was left free for the farmers' produce. On the opposite side, Monty put up shelves and counters, made from packing-box lumber. Miss Mattie proudly arranged her stock in orderly array. And, for the first time, each article carried a price tag.

This was Monty's idea. Miss Mattie listened sympathetically while he explained it. Old Man Brown listened, too.

"It'll make it easier for us, and it'll please the farmers," Monty argued. "They never see cash money for what they raise. But it's *worth* money. So why don't we put a cash price on it? Instead of saying we'll give a suit of clothes for a load of corn, we could say we'd give four dollars. Then let him pick out a four-dollar suit, or four dollars' worth of anything he wants."

"We've never done it that way," Miss Mattie observed. "It was always a case of what we wanted to sell most. If we were overstocked on shoes, we'd offer him shoes; or maybe a suit, if we'd got lots of suits. We didn't give him a free choice."

"I know, and that's just what I want to change. Why shouldn't he have a free choice? He would if he had the cash in hand, and his stuff is as good as cash. And about being overstocked—well, it don't seem to me that being overstocked is good business. Why can't we do some figuring before we make out our orders? Keep track of what we have the most call for, and buy more of that and less of the things they don't need so much."

Mr. Brown put in an unexpected word. "Reckon we got enough collar buttons on hand to last till Judgment Day. Don't seem to be no call for collar buttons no more."

"Well, of course not," Monty said eagerly. "All our customers have *got* collar buttons. You don't wear a collar button out. Unless you lose one, you never have to buy another. It's not right to force things they don't need on people."

"I think you're right, Monty," Miss Mattie said. "And I like your notion of putting cash prices on everything—their stuff and ours. Only I don't quite see how you'd handle it. You can't really give them cash. They might go out and spend it somewhere else. Captain Boughton would never stand for that."

"No, I'm afraid not. We'd have to keep it so no real money changes hands. What I'd do, I'd give them a due bill, good for so much in dollars. They'd take it across the store, look at the prices there, and spend it any way they wanted to. It'd be awful handy for the little things that make so much trouble now—thread and pins and such. Give a farmer's wife a dollar due bill, and I bet you she'd enjoy herself all morning. We might even get rid of a few collar buttons that way." He laughed.

"It looks like a grand scheme to me, Monty," Miss Mattie said warmly. "I'm in favor of trying it."

There was a little pause, while they waited for Old Man Brown to speak. After all, he *was* the manager.

At last he nodded. "It sounds all right to me. Captain don't like to be bothered. You young folks just go ahead and fix it up to suit yourselves."

As Monty had foreseen, the new system appealed strongly to the farmers. Even though they never saw the money, it was gratifying to have a cash figure placed on the fruits of their labors.

The women customers liked the new plan. Even better, they liked the attractive new displays of merchandise. Miss Mattie managed a sit-down bench for shoe-fitting and a mirror for trying on hats. The place no longer looked like a cluttered jungle. It was a real store now.

As the months went by, Monty took on more and more of the manager's duties. Miss Mattie liked selling best. It was Monty who bargained with the farmers, and Monty who kept track of the stock and made out new orders for the wholesalers' salesmen. When Mr. Brown's failing eyesight made the bookkeeping difficult, Monty offered to take over the accounts.

"I don't know the first thing about it," he said frankly. "But I can learn if you'll show me, Mr. Brown."

The old man was glad to agree. His lessons were not very helpful, but Captain Boughton loaned Monty an up-to-date textbook on business accounting. The new boy was sleeping in the store now, and Monty had a room in the Diefendorf cottage. There, night after night, he studied until he turned himself into a first-class bookkeeper.

His interest did not end there. The whole field of merchandising fascinated him. In storekeeping he had found his life work, the "something a man can put his heart into." He bought or borrowed every business book he could lay hands on. Among them was a little volume on business letter-writing. With it as a guide, he worked earnestly to bring correctness into his everyday speech. A big merchant, as he meant to be some day, must not talk like a day laborer.

The years that went so swiftly past were the Civil War years. Michigan boys, like boys all over the North, were marching off behind the fife and drum. Young Montgomery Ward stuck soberly to his job, suppressing whatever dreams of military glory he may have had. He was earning good money now and sending most of it home to Niles. By the time he was twenty-one, he figured, his father would have enough on hand to open the Beehive store. With his duty to his family done, he would be free to offer his services to his country.

Monty's twenty-first birthday came in February, 1865. The Civil War ended in April of that same year. In after life, he was to show his patriotism in every way that a civilian can, even though he was never called upon to show it on the battlefield.

Mr. Brown's health forced his retirement in the winter of 1864. Monty took his place as manager, at $100 a month and board. This was a fantastic salary for a young man of only twenty. The Captain declared that what Monty had done for the store made him worth every cent of it.

What he had done for the store was the talk of the town. It was not alone that he had made the place as attractive as any Main Street establishment. The amazing change was in the merchandise offered to his farmer customers.

To the Chicago wholesale houses, the farm trade had always been an outlet for damaged, shopworn stock. Anything was good enough for the hayseeds. Storekeepers like Mr. Carver heartily agreed. The first salesman who found Monty in charge got a rude shock.

Young Ward led the man to the back of the store. There he displayed a packing box half-full of shoes: men's, women's, and children's. One by one Monty held them up.

"Look at this. The stitching has run off, and the sole is hanging by a thread. And this one. Feel inside. Nails half an inch long to stick in some little girl's foot. Yes, I know they can be hammered down. Why weren't they hammered down before you unloaded them on us? And here's a pair—the left foot must be two sizes bigger than the right. Here's one with half the buttons missing, too."

He tossed them back into the box.

"As soon as the box is full, I'm shipping it to your warehouse, collect. And I'll expect full credit for the lot."

The salesman looked startled. "But, Ward, you can't do that! With trade like yours, what difference does it make? Of course," he added, "I might be able to shade the price a little, if that's what you're after."

"It's not what I'm after," Ward said flatly. "We pay for perfect merchandise, and we want perfect merchandise. I'm not interested in what you think about my trade. Your house will give us what we order and pay for, or we'll go elsewhere."

His firm attitude brought results. The quality of the merchandise improved, and his farm customers came to depend upon it. "You never get stung at Cap Boughton's place," they told their neighbors. And more and more of the neighbors brought their business there.

Monty and Miss Mattie gave a good deal of thought to their customers' convenience. The farm families, making an all-day stay, usually brought cold lunches with them. These were eaten in the wagons outside the store. It was Monty who arranged a picnic grove for them.

Behind the store was a wilderness of underbrush, topped by some fine old walnut trees. Monty cleared out the bushes and knocked together some tables and benches. Drinking water was available from the store's well. The families could eat there, visiting around the long tables. The children could play in safety while their elders shopped.

The picnic grove did as much as anything to win popularity for the store and its young master. It was also the scene of a meeting that was to affect Montgomery Ward's whole life.

5

IN THE PICNIC GROVE

One hot afternoon in July of 1865, a young army officer came into the store. He was extremely handsome in his blue cavalry uniform, with a magnificent sword and epaulettes dripping with gold fringe. He approached Monty with a smile.

"Good afternoon, sir. You are the manager here? I'm Major Robert Thorne, of Kalamazoo. I've come to ask permission to trespass."

"How do you do, Major Thorne." Monty was polite but puzzled. "To trespass? I'm afraid I don't understand."

"Then I'll hasten to explain. I am escorting some Kalamazoo ladies who will take the steamer to Chicago. It appears we must wait some time while the steamer is loaded. It is infernally hot aboard. We would be most grateful if you would allow us to wait in the pleasant grove behind your store. The sign says that it is for customers only, but I hope you can be persuaded to make an exception in our favor. In fact," he ended with a laugh, "the hope was so strong that I have already seated the ladies there. But if you object—"

"Of course I don't object," Monty broke in. "I had to put up the sign, because the young people of the town were crowding out my customers. It will be a pleasure to accommodate your party, Major. Please tell the ladies to make themselves at home."

"Good!" The young major dropped his formal manner, to Monty's great relief. He had done his best to imitate it, but it was something of a strain.

"You see," Major Thorne went on confidentially, "it means a lot to me for this trip to go smoothly. The train trip down from Kalamazoo was not too comfortable, and this unexpected wait is trying. One of the ladies is—well, I hope she's going to be my mother-in-law. I'd like to make a good impression on her. My leave is short; I don't have much time, and—well, there it is. You're doing me a favor, and Ellen, too. The poor dear is pretty well worn out with this heat. And her mother is already short-tempered about it."

"We'll make them as comfortable as we can," Monty said sympathetically. This clear-eyed, pleasant young officer with a romantic problem had won his instant liking. "We haven't any refreshments here, but I could send the boy uptown for some ice cream. Your young lady is with her mother, then?"

"Naturally, or I wouldn't be here. Her sister's along, too," Thorne added carelessly. "The ice cream would be a blessing. Tell him for four of us—no, make it five. You'll join us, won't you, Mr.—Ward, is it? Please come.

Mrs. Cobb was wondering about a store with a picnic grove. You could entertain her a little while we wait. She's not a very patient person. Unless you're too busy?"

Ward glanced around the store. It was a quiet afternoon. Miss Mattie and the new clerk seemed to have the situation well in hand.

"I can spare a few minutes," he agreed.

He whistled for Rusty, the odd-job boy, and sent him to the ice cream parlor. Then he turned to his visitor. "He'll bring it out to the grove. Shall we go along?"

Monty's liking for his new acquaintance deepened with every minute. Thorne was seven or eight years his senior, but in many ways he was far more boyish.

"Look at her!" he said fondly as they approached the little group under the trees. "Tell me, old man, did you ever see a face so beautiful in all your dreams?"

Monty might have said truthfully that he had never seen two such faces. Mrs. Cobb herself was a handsome woman, but her two daughters were lovely beyond believing. Although one was very young—not more than sixteen, Monty guessed—the sisters were very much alike. Both were dark-haired and dark-eyed, with the exquisite rose-flushed cheeks of their own Michigan peaches. The elder sister was more elaborately dressed, with her hair piled high under a flowered bonnet and her skirts sweeping the ground. The younger girl wore the simple ankle-length organdy of a schoolgirl, her hair tied back by a ribbon.

It was amusingly plain that Major Thorne had eyes for only one of the sisters. He introduced Monty first to Mrs. Cobb and then to Miss Ellen.

"Mr. Ward is having some ice cream brought to us," he explained eagerly. "He says at the rate the steamer is loading, we'll have a couple of hours to wait. Wouldn't you like to turn your back to the sun, Mrs. Cobb? I'm afraid it will be in your eyes in a minute or two. Let me help you."

Under cover of the move, the younger girl spoke shyly to Monty.

"I'm Elizabeth Cobb, Mr. Ward. It's very kind of you to take us in." She moved to make a place for him beside her. "I've been watching those children over there— they're having such a good time on the swing. Are they yours?"

Monty glanced at the small boy swinging his smaller sister at the far side of the grove. Except for the children, the grove was deserted.

"Oh, no, I'm not married," he said hastily. "Those are some farm children—their parents are inside the store. Shopping gets tiresome for the littlest ones, so I fixed up the swing for them. There's a teeter-totter board, too. If you'd come around noon, you'd have seen six or eight families out here. But most of them have started for home by this time of day."

"Are all your customers farmers, then?" she asked. She sounded so interested that before he knew it Monty was telling her all about the store. Presently her mother joined in with more questions. Major Thorne, throwing Monty a grateful glance, drew his Ellen aside for a low-toned conversation.

The arrival of the ice cream brought the company together again. But after it was finished, it was only natural for Monty to offer to show the visitors around the store. When Miss Ellen declared she was too comfortable to move, Major Thorne stayed behind to keep her company.

Monty prolonged the inspection trip until the steamer whistled. Both Mrs. Cobb and her younger daughter took a keen interest in what they saw. They stopped for a pleasant chat with Miss Mattie. Mrs. Cobb won her heart by admiring the good taste of the women's wear Miss Mattie had chosen.

"I never could see why farm women had to look so dowdy," the Kalamazoo lady remarked. "You're doing a fine thing to give them clothes they can wear with pride. I wonder why no one ever thought of it before?"

At the sound of the steamer whistle, Monty hurried his guests down to the pier. The Major and Miss Ellen were already there. The Cobbs, after graceful good-bys, went ahead, but Thorne stopped at the gangplank to wring Monty's hand.

"You gave me the chance I've been hoping for," he said boyishly. "I popped the question, and she said yes! Now if I can just win over the old lady—"

"You will," Monty assured him. "And congratulations,

Major! Please give Miss Ellen my best wishes for her future happiness."

"She's as grateful as I am, Ward. Oh, by the way, they'll be back on the Friday steamer. Would you see that they get aboard the Kalamazoo train all right? I won't be with them. Have to get back to the regiment, you know."

"I'll be glad to look after them, of course. But aren't you home for good? The war is over."

"Not for me." The young officer laughed. "I'm a Regular Army man, attached to General Custer's staff. The word is that we're being sent to the western plains for a spell of Indian fighting. Well, good-by, Ward. I hope we meet again sometime. But even if we never do, I'll always remember you."

They stood together, two handsome, stalwart young men who were to be lifelong friends. Neither knew it then. But it was with real regret that they parted after that first meeting.

Monty watched until the steamer disappeared into the misty distance of Lake Michigan. Mrs. Cobb had gone to her cabin, but Major Thorne and the sisters lingered at the rail, waving until they were out of sight.

Shading his eyes for the last faint glimpse, Montgomery Ward was startled by a poetic thought. He was not a poetic young man, and such thoughts did not come easily to him. But the two girls were—they really were like two summer roses. Or—no, that was wrong. Like a full-blown rose and a graceful bud.

The steamer faded from sight. Sighing, he turned away. There was work to be done—work with onions, and potatoes, and a doubtful shipment of gents' furnishings. Captain Boughton did not pay his efficient young manager to waste the afternoon mooning over rosebuds that grew beyond his reach.

ON THE ROAD

One of the salesmen who called on Monty was from the Chicago wholesale house of Field, Palmer & Leiter. The company also operated a retail store, which is now the famous Marshall Field's.

The salesman-friend thought Monty was wasted in St. Joseph. Through his influence came the offer of a job in his firm's Chicago store. The salary was half what Captain Boughton was paying. But, as the salesman urged, there was no future here. "You've reached the top of the tree, Monty. But in Chicago there *is* no top. You can climb as high as you are able."

Ward thought it over. This was as good a time as any to leave Michigan. He had steadfastly sent most of his earnings home to Niles. Now at last, Pa Ward was about to realize his long dream. Within the month, the Beehive Emporium would open for business.

The older girls were married, but the younger ones and the brother were to be clerks. The little store would provide the family a living without any help from Monty. With a clear conscience, he could devote all his efforts to his own future.

He was not long in deciding to accept the Chicago offer. Late in the autumn of 1865 he took Captain Boughton's steamer across the lake. He was not yet twenty-two years old.

Monty spent two years behind the counters of Field, Palmer & Leiter. This time, there was no gratifying rise to the top of the tree. Marshall Field had his own ideas for running his big modern city store. He needed no suggestions from an obscure young Michigan clerk. Monty gave satisfaction in his clerking job, and stayed in it.

This was not enough for an ambitious young man. He had several friends among the traveling salesmen, or "drummers" as they were called. They told him there were better chances on the road.

He applied for and got a position traveling for a Chicago wholesale house. A little later, he changed to a better one with the St. Louis firm of Walter M. Smith & Company.

With his headquarters in St. Louis, he traveled regularly in Illinois, Missouri, and Kansas. Monty was the newest salesman. That meant that he was given the least desirable territory. Not for him the big towns, with their comfortable hotels and decent meals. His customers were in the rural villages, where the one hotel was likely to be a horror.

Nowadays, every such village has its up-to-date hotel or motor court. In Monty's time, small town hotels were bad beyond belief. Cramped, stuffy rooms, lumpy beds, wretched meals—these were the lot of the "drummers," who were the usual guests. The solid citizens thought very little of drummers anyway. It was only once in a great while that a friendly customer would ask Monty home to supper with his family.

More often, after his business was finished, he faced a long, lonely evening. There were no movies, no radio or television to distract him. His room would be unheated in winter, stifling hot in summer. All he could do would be to sit in the dingy hotel lobby until bedtime. If he had luck, he might find another luckless salesman or two to chat with.

It was a dreary life and a lonely one. Yet with only his own thoughts for company, Montgomery Ward was driven to some hard thinking, the results of which would amaze the world. It might never have happened if life on the road had been pleasanter for him.

He was always glad when it was time to report back to his St. Louis headquarters. He came in one winter night hungry and tired, but with a gratifying sheaf of orders.

A glance at his watch showed him he was too late for supper at his city boardinghouse. This had been a good trip, and he was feeling extravagant. He decided to allow himself the luxury of a bang-up meal before he went home.

He checked his heavy sample cases in the station and hurried off to a first-rate hotel.

The big dining room seemed to be filled. He hesitated

a minute, dazzled by the gaslight sparkling on snowy linen and polished silver. The head waiter came up to him.

"I'm afraid I don't have a table for one right now, sir. If you wouldn't mind waiting a few minutes . . . ?"

Monty was already regretting his impulse. His clothes were wrinkled and mussed from the long train ride, and he felt out of place among these well-dressed diners.

"Never mind." He was turning toward the door when a young man at a nearby table beckoned.

"I'd be glad to share my table," he told the waiter. "Ask the gentleman if he'll do me the honor of joining me."

Monty started. The voice, and even more the manner —what did they remind him of? Puzzled, he moved over to the man.

"It's very kind of you, sir, but I can easily go elsewhere," he began.

"Nonsense! I'm glad to have company. Sit down, Mr. —well, I'll be hanged! It's Ward, isn't it?" He jumped up and held out his hand. "The lad who saved my life in St. Joe! Don't tell me you don't know me?"

Monty stared a minute and then grasped the hand. "Major Thorne! It sounded like you, but I couldn't be sure—you look so different out of uniform. Have you left the army then?"

"Long ago; the winter after I met you. My beloved mama-in-law saw to that. She wasn't going to have her darling daughter away out in an Indian-fighting post, in danger of being scalped any minute. If you remember Mother Cobb, you remember what a dragon she is. That's why I say you saved my life that day. You gave me the first chance I had had to speak to Ellen without her mother hearing every word. She's a dear old soul really, but in those days she frightened me to death."

"She frightened me, too," Monty admitted. "Of course, I only saw her that one afternoon. Oh, yes, and for a few minutes when I put her and her daughters aboard the train the next week. I haven't seen any of them since. So you and Miss Ellen are married?"

"For five years. We have two boys," Thorne said proudly. "I'm in the lumber business in Chicago now. You must come and see us if you ever get to town. Do you live here in St. Louis? I didn't even know you'd left St. Joe. I might have guessed you would, though. Mother Cobb said the town would never hold you. 'That's an ambitious young man with big ideas,' she declared. 'He'll go far.' "

"Did she say that?" Monty could not hide his pleasure. But he added rather sadly, "I'm afraid she was wrong. I certainly haven't gone very far yet."

"Well, what are we standing for? Sit down, and let's hear all about you."

Monty settled himself at the table and gave the waiter his order.

"There's not much to tell," he said then. "I had a couple of years in the Field retail store. For two years now I've been on the road with a drygoods line. And that's all."

"Of course it's not all," his friend protested. "You're young; you can't be thirty yet. First thing you know, they'll make you sales manager."

"I used to hope I could work up to that," Monty admitted. "Now—I'm not sure I want it. I—I have something else in mind. Something entirely different."

"What is it? One of those big ideas of yours? Let's hear it."

Monty looked uncomfortable. "Oh, it's nothing—I

haven't even got it all worked out in my own mind yet. I'd lots rather hear about you and the lumber business. Did you say you're located in Chicago?"

The waiter brought his food then, and the two men chatted until the meal was finished.

"I'm staying here in the hotel," Thorne remarked as they rose. "Came to St. Louis to straighten out a freight shipment. I'm going back tomorrow. Why don't we go up to my room for a while? I was afraid I'd have a dull evening to kill. It's a treat to have someone to talk to."

7

MONTY'S BIG IDEA

Once upstairs, Thorne returned to an earlier topic.

"This big idea of yours—I confess I'm curious. Of course I don't want to pry."

Monty hesitated. He had never spoken of this to anyone. But the good dinner, the pleasant surroundings, the friendly talk—these had put him into a confiding mood. And most of all he felt himself responding to Thorne's sincere interest.

"I'd like to tell you," he began slowly. "But it's a crazy scheme, I guess. Something that's never been done. I expect you'll say it can't be done. But if I can save enough money, I want to start a business of my own."

"And what's crazy about that? It's how I got into the lumber business, saving from my army pay."

"Yes, but lumber *is* a business," Monty said soberly. "This one of mine,—well, it's not. Not a regular business. No one has ever tried it. It's just something I've figured out, sitting around with nothing to do in the evenings. But to save my soul, I can't see why it wouldn't work!"

"Well, out with it, man! What kind of business is it?"

"I had to make up my own name for it," Monty said

shyly. "I call it the mail-order business. If you really want to hear—all right, you asked for it."

He drew a deep breath. "First I have to tell you how I feel about farmers. You remember Cap Boughton's store? All our customers were country people. I liked them. I tried to see they got good value for what they brought us. Now I've traveled a lot since then. I've seen the way the farmers get treated in the stores in my territory. 'Anything's good enough for hayseeds,' they used to say back in St. Joe. They say the same thing out here. It made me mad then. And it makes me mad now!"

"I see it does." Major Thorne laughed. "What do you want to do then? Open a store for farmers?"

"Not a store." Ward's voice grew very earnest. "Major, you know how retail prices are set. The storekeeper pays the wholesale price. Then he adds in his expenses— rent, heat, clerk hire, and so on. And then—*then* he adds in his profit."

"Yes, of course. What's wrong with that?"

"There's nothing wrong with it in the big towns, where the storekeeper has competition. Remember he sets his own profit. If he puts it too high, the man across the street can undersell him and take away his customers. But in the towns I visit, there may not be a man across the street. Maybe there's only one drygoods store or one shoe store in the village. The storekeeper can put his profit at 20 per cent, or 30 per cent, or 40 per cent. And the farmers have to pay it."

"Why can't the farmer put up his profits, too?" Thorne asked. "He brings his produce to sell, doesn't he?"

"He does, and the town folks tell him how much it's worth," Ward answered. "If he doesn't take it, what's he going to do with his load? Haul it home again? No, I tell you, the farmer is caught. He has to take what's offered him. He has to pay what's asked. Often he pays it for faded, damaged merchandise. And everybody thinks that's all right. After all, he's only a farmer!"

Thorne's brow wrinkled. "Couldn't he take his business to a larger town?"

"You wouldn't ask that if you'd seen the mud roads

in my territory. No, he has to stick to his nearest town and put up with what farmers have always put up with. I think it's time something was done about it. And, Thorne, I honestly think I could do something."

"Now we're coming to it." Thorne smiled. "You've shown me your problem. Now let's see your remedy. Not a store, you said?"

"No. A mail-order business. I told you you'd call it crazy," Monty warned. "But this is how it would work. I've got a list of farmers' names I've made up while I was traveling—got them from the post offices mostly or from my customers. I'd write these people letters and enclose a list of goods and prices. The farmers would mail me in their orders. I'd fill them by buying direct from the wholesalers."

"At no profit? That would be nice for the farmers, but I don't know how long you'd stay in business."

Ward laughed. "I'm not that crazy, Major. Certainly I'd take a profit. But it would be a reasonable one. Say 10 per cent after expenses. That's a whole lot less than these village storekeepers charge. And I'd give my customers good sound merchandise they could depend on."

There was a pause. Monty broke it by saying uneasily, "Well, there it is. I can see you don't think much of the scheme."

"I wouldn't say that. I'm just trying to figure it out. Would you expect your customers to send their money before they saw the goods? How would they know they'd get what you promised? I don't think your farmer friends would relish buying a pig in a poke that way."

"But I'd give them their money back if they weren't satisfied," Monty explained. "Yes, it would have to be a cash business. I can get lower prices from the wholesalers with cash in hand. Of course, I'll have to have some cash of my own to get started. I'll have to buy my first stock, and there'll be stamps and such. But my expense won't be anything like a storekeeper's. I can handle everything myself—at least until it begins to grow. I've got almost enough put by now to make the start. But—oh, I don't know. I can see you don't think it would work."

"You can't see anything of the sort," the Major said warmly. "I don't know whether it would work or not. Nobody can know until it's tried. But it's certainly the most original idea I've come across in a blue moon. And I will say this. You've convinced me. If I were a farmer, I wouldn't hesitate to be your first customer."

"You really mean that?" Monty's face glowed. His lonely life had given him no chance to make close friends. Once or twice he had hinted at his idea to salesmen he met on the road. They had all scoffed at the idea of doing anything for the hayseeds.

Now, for the first time, he had explained it all in detail. Major Thorne was an intelligent, educated man. He had not ridiculed the scheme. Instead, he had shown confidence in it. This confidence gave Monty the new determination he needed to go ahead.

"I'm going to do it," he declared as they parted an hour later. "All I need now is a job that will keep me here in town all the time. I couldn't operate it while I'm out on the road. I'll see if my firm will give me office work of some kind—bookkeeping, maybe. That would leave me my evenings and week ends free to work on my own scheme. I can't afford to give up a steady job until I see how it goes."

"Of course not," Thorne agreed. "You're lucky to have no one else depending on you, though. When a man has a wife and babies to take care of, he's not so free to launch out into something new. Well, the best of luck, Ward. And let me know how you get on with it."

"I'll do that. You may see me in Chicago one of these days. If I can't get an office job here, I'll go back there, where I know more people. I could operate just as well from there, wouldn't you think?"

"Better," Thorne answered. "You could reach the Michigan and Wisconsin farmers from there, too. It seems to me Chicago would be your best location."

"Well, we'll see."

They repeated their good-bys. Then, with a light heart, Monty set out for his boardinghouse. His mail-order scheme had won warm approval. And, whether it succeeded or failed, he had found a friend.

8

SUNSHINE OVER KALAMAZOO

Monty's St. Louis employers had no office job for him. He wrote to several Chicago firms and was lucky enough to get an offer from Partridge Brothers, a wholesale dry-goods house.

His work was that of a buyer. This meant that instead of selling to stores, he bought merchandise from the manufacturers for his firm to resell. It was a new field for Ward and one he needed to know about. Buying would be as important in his new business as selling. He learned all he could and was grateful for the generous salary that helped him to save while he was learning.

With his savings, he began cautiously to do a little buying on his own account.

For his firm, he bought large shipments on the customary credit terms. But once in a while a manufacturer would have an odd lot to dispose of—quantities too small to interest the wholesalers. It might be a few dozen pairs of socks or a discontinued line of men's underwear. They could be had very cheaply for spot cash. Monty produced the cash and added the items to his growing stockpile. It grew slowly, for such bargains were not to be had every day. But he was a patient man, and he could afford to wait.

Life in Chicago would have been easier than life on the road if he had given himself time to enjoy it. He looked up the Thornes as soon as he arrived and sometimes went to their house for supper. But usually his evenings were spent in his boardinghouse room planning and figuring, getting ready for the great adventure.

One day he surprised Thorne by accepting an invitation. Major Thorne was taking his eldest son to spend some weeks in Kalamazoo with his grandparents.

"I'll be coming back on the night train myself," he told Monty. "Why don't you come along? A day's outing will do you good. What with working all day for Partridge and all night for yourself, you're turning into a regular hermit. It won't hurt you to cut loose for once. I don't believe you've been to Michigan since you came back to Chicago."

"Oh, yes, I run over to Niles to see my family once in a while," Ward answered. "But I haven't been to Kalamazoo since I was a boy. I'd like to see it again. I wouldn't want to impose on your mother-in-law, though."

"She'd be delighted. The old lady has asked about you several times. She was quite cross when you couldn't come to dinner that time she visited us. You'll go then? Fine. We'll meet you at the station Sunday morning."

Father and son were waiting when Monty arrived. Charles Thorne was a sturdy three-year-old with his father's frank eyes and friendly smile. He greeted Monty with a whoop of joy.

"Uncle Monty! I'm going to sleep in Mama's little room at Gramma's. And Gramp don't care if the dog sleeps in bed with me, but Gramma does. Do you think I can sneak him in, Uncle Monty? Do you?"

"I bet you can." Ward swung the little boy to his shoulder. "Tell me about the dog. What's his name?"

"Never mind dogs. Here's our train." Robert Thorne picked up the child's carpetbag and heaved it aboard. Monty followed and set the little boy down on a plush seat. Charlie promptly pulled himself up on his knees and glued his face to the window.

The two men took the facing seat, and the train pulled out. "He's set for the trip," the father remarked. "Well, so I did get you out of your shell for a day! I'm surprised. I thought at the last minute you'd decide you couldn't spare the time."

Monty grinned back at him. "This is a celebration, Bob. I've done it. Yep, that's what I mean. Built up all the stock I need for a beginning. All paid for and ready to fill orders. I spent most of Friday night addressing envelopes for price lists. And yesterday I mailed them out."

He paused, enjoying Thorne's astonishment.

"You've really taken the plunge then! You didn't tell me it was so close."

"I wanted to surprise you," Monty answered.

"Well, you have. So now you're in business for yourself. How does it feel?"

"I don't know yet. After all, I'm not in business until the first orders come in. Maybe there won't be any. At best, it'll be quite a while before I can be sure how it's going. I'm holding on to my Partridge job until I *am* sure."

Eager discussion filled the train ride until they reached Kalamazoo. Thorne was almost as excited as Monty. He had approved the plan from the start. His encouragement had done much to decide Ward to try it. Now he wanted to hear every detail.

They left the train and walked down the dusty street. Little Charlie broke away and turned into a gate. Ward's eyes widened as he took in the big wooden house with its gingerbread trimmings.

Robert Thorne smiled. "Quite a mansion, isn't it? My wife's grandfather built it back in the early days, when he put up the first sawmill. Ellen's people have always been in the lumber business, like mine. There's Mother Cobb now."

Mrs. Cobb was waiting on the porch, little Charlie clinging to her hand. She had grown stouter, and her eyes were even more piercing. They swept over Monty now, as Thorne introduced him.

"Never would have known you," she said flatly. "Good gracious, young man, you were nothing but a country jake then. In looks, I mean. But now—well, maybe it's the

city clothes and the city haircut. You look like you'd
never been out of Chicago. I wouldn't have believed it."

Monty managed a smile as he took her hand. "I guess
I was pretty green then, Mrs. Cobb. I hope you think
I've changed for the better."

"No question of it," she answered briskly. "I knew
you were smart. The way you ran that farmers' store
proved it. I said then you'd get ahead. But I never said
you'd turn out good-looking. I declare, if you're not
downright handsome."

They were entering the house now, and she raised her
voice. "Elizabeth! Come and see— Oh, I forgot. She's
out in the grape arbor with Dad. You go bring them in,
Bob. Take Mr. Ward along; Dad will want to show off
his prize grapes. Tell them dinner's ready."

A charming picture met the eyes of the two young
men as they approached the grape arbor. Elizabeth Cobb
was standing on a tall ladder snipping heavy bunches of
purple grapes and handing them down to her father. The
vine leaves made a lacework of sun and shadow over the
laughing young face.

She came down the ladder in haste, blushing furiously.
Young ladies did not climb ladders in that Victorian day
—certainly not in the presence of strange young men.

The blush only made the lovely face lovelier. At sight
of it, Monty Ward lost all his new self-confidence. He
was buyer for a leading Chicago firm and newly launched
as head of his own business. He was smartly dressed from

63

the fashionable Field store. The critical Mrs. Cobb had just pronounced him handsome. For all this, he felt himself an awkward country yokel, tongue-tied before such breath-taking beauty.

Like the princess in the fairy tale, Elizabeth Cobb was as good as she was beautiful. Her sharp-tongued mother had seen to it that their extraordinary good looks did not spoil her girls. "Handsome is as handsome does" had been drummed into them from childhood. Any signs of vanity were ruthlessly suppressed. Being pretty did not excuse a girl from being industrious, and gentle, and thoughtful of others. So Mama Cobb had preached, and the result was a credit to her.

Elizabeth greeted Monty with the same shy friendliness he remembered so well from their first meeting. Her father, a vigorous businessman whose hobby was grape-growing, did most of the talking. Mostly he talked of his grapes.

"Are you in lumber, too, Mr. Ward?" he asked presently.

"No, I'm with a drygoods firm," Monty was beginning, when Thorne interrupted him.

"Tell him about your mail-order business, Monty. Dad, this boy has thought up something brand new, right out of his own head. A kind of business you never heard of. Tell him, Monty."

Stumblingly at first, Ward began explaining his plan.

Before he had gone very far, he was interrupted by the arrival of little Charlie.

"Gramma wants you, Gramp. Dinner's almost ready, and she's says you gotta put on a collar and tie before you sit down 'cause it's Sunday, and we got company."

Mr. Cobb grunted. "All right, sonny. I'll be right in." He glanced toward the bench, where the grapes were heaped in rich confusion. "Got to get these grapes packed in the baskets first, though."

Bob Thorne spoke quickly. "We'll do that, Dad. You go ahead to the house. The three of us will finish them off in no time."

As soon as Mr. Cobb had gone with the little boy, Thorne took a pipe out of his pocket.

"If you folks won't tell on me," he drawled, "I'm going down behind the barn and steal a few puffs. Mother Cobb doesn't approve of the nasty habit I picked up in the army. See you at dinner."

He caught Monty's eye and winked, and then was gone.

Elizabeth smiled. "Ellen lets Bob smoke at home, but she daren't tell Mama. Now if you'll hand me the bunches one by one, I'll pack them. And do go on with what you were telling Dad, Mr. Ward—about selling to the farmers by mail. It sounds like an awfully good thing for them."

Under her sweet sympathy, he forgot his embarrassment and poured out all his eager hopes. Afterward, he wondered anxiously if he had talked too much about himself. Elizabeth did not seem to think so. They spent no more than ten minutes alone together, busily packing grapes. It was the happiest ten minutes Monty had ever known.

9

FLAME AND SMOKE
OVER CHICAGO

At the dinner table, Mr. Cobb returned to the subject of Monty's new business. He was interested but not altogether convinced.

"Farmers are a pretty hardheaded lot," he observed. "I know, because I do business with them. They're awfully suspicious that you're trying to cheat them. And this scheme of yours could easily sound like a kind of bunco game."

"It could easily be one," Monty said frankly. "My father was a farmer, and he got cheated buying a store by mail. I won't blame them if they're suspicious of me at first. But I'm offering to give them their money back if they're not satisfied. I'll do it quick, by return mail. They won't even have to claim the merchandise isn't any good. It *will* be good, that's sure. But if they change their mind for any reason, they can have their money back and no questions asked."

Mr. Cobb nodded. "Well, you can't do more than that. You say your stock is all in drygoods? Seems to me you ought to get a little more variety into it. Harness, now.

The farmer pays a fearful price for that in the village store."

"And tinware," Mrs. Cobb put in. "You don't want to forget the kitchen, Mr. Ward."

"I'm not forgetting it," Monty answered. "I'm starting with drygoods because I know drygoods best. That's what I've been working with, you know. I've met the manufacturers, and they give me a chance at bargains in that line. Later, I hope to add housewares. I hadn't thought about harness, Mr. Cobb, but it's a fine idea."

"What do you have on your list?" Elizabeth asked. "Work clothes and things like that?"

Ward shook his head. "Nothing so big, I'm afraid. I thought it was better to start with small items, so I could get in as many as possible. Yard goods, paper collars, gloves and mittens, socks and stockings, needles, thread, pins, handkerchiefs—here. This will show you."

He pulled one of his printed price lists from his pocket and passed it around.

"I must say these prices amaze me," Mrs. Cobb remarked. "Seven yards of canton flannel for a dollar! I pay twenty cents a yard for it here in Kalamazoo. It's good quality, though."

"So is mine good quality," Monty said firmly. "I won't touch the shoddy stuff. That's why it has taken me so long to build up my stock. The price has to be right, but the goods have to be right, too, or they're no use to me."

"Where do you keep your stock?" Thorne inquired. "Did you have to rent warehouse space?"

"No, I was lucky there. Partridge Brothers keep their teams at a livery stable on Rush Street. The owner has a big hayloft—bigger than he needs. He lets me have a corner of it for nothing. Of course, the little things I have now don't take up much room. When I really get going, I'll have to find a place of my own."

"Then your expenses start," Mr. Cobb chuckled.

"Yes, but I'll never have the expense a retail merchant has," Monty said earnestly. "My customers won't come in the place; I don't have to worry about a good location or fancy fixtures. And remember I'm cutting out the middleman's profits. The goods move straight from the factory to the purchaser, with only the one profit in between. Mine. And I'm putting that at 5 per cent after expenses on some items and 10 per cent on others. Nothing higher."

"Nothing higher than 10 per cent?" Mr. Cobb looked doubtful. "That's mighty low. Now I'd figure it—"

Monty listened respectfully to Mr. Cobb's views. Then he explained quietly but confidently why he thought his figures were right. The discussion carried through pie and cake, to the end of the meal.

As they rose from the table, Mr. Cobb remarked, "Well, time for my Sunday afternoon nap. Bob, why don't you hitch up and drive Ward around town? There's been a lot of new building in Kalamazoo lately. Show this city fellow what a live little town we've got."

Monty stole a glance toward Elizabeth, who was helping her mother clear the table.

"You do that, Bob," Mrs. Cobb cut in. "After we do the dishes, Lizzie and I are going to take little Charlie over to Uncle Jerome's to see his young cousins. Everybody be back here in time for supper, now."

With a sigh, Monty followed Thorne to the stable. His friend gave him a hearty slap on the back.

"What did you expect, young fellow? That you could go buggy-riding with Elizabeth? The old lady's a dragon, always was. You're doing better than I did when I was courting Ellen. You had ten minutes alone with a Cobb daughter—and only on your second meeting, too. You can thank me for that."

"My third meeting," Monty corrected him. "And I do thank you, Bob, from the bottom of my heart. She's —well, I never met a girl like her. Is she—is she engaged or anything?"

"Not that I've heard of. And Ellen would know. Oh, of course she has all the young men of Kalamazoo at her feet. But Mother Cobb scares them off. I remember when I tackled her about marrying Ellen. I'd sooner have faced General Sherman in one of his famous rages."

"Yes, but you did it. And she let Ellen marry you. She seems to like you well enough now."

Thorne laughed. "We get along fine, although I still jump when she speaks to me. But you're off to a better start than I was, Monty. She approves of you as a rising young businessman. Of course, whether she'd approve of you as a son-in-law—!"

Monty's jaw set. "I'm in no position to find out right now. But if things work out the way I hope—if my new business is a success—well, I won't be afraid to tackle her!"

The family came together again for a cold supper at sunset. Afterward, they moved out to the big veranda. A hot, dry wind was blowing from the west. It grew stronger after darkness fell. Mrs. Cobb, coming back from putting little Charlie to bed, sniffed the heavy air.

"Seems to me I smell something burning," she remarked. "I hope it's not a forest fire. This has been such a dry summer. The woods are like tinder. Do you smell it, Dad?"

Her husband sniffed. "Something burning, all right. But it's a long way off, or we'd see the light."

He yawned, and Monty moved uneasily. He knew that their visitors were keeping the family up past their usual bedtime. There was no train back to Chicago until midnight. He wondered if he should propose to Bob that they go down to the depot and wait there. Or would the Cobbs think that was bad manners?

"But I do see a light!" Elizabeth said suddenly. "Look, just beyond the trees there. And it's getting brighter."

"The moon coming up—" her father began, and stopped.

No Michigan moon shone with that smoky red glare,

spreading now until it lighted the western sky. And every minute the smell of burning grew stronger.

"It's a fire, all right, and a big one!" Robert Thorne began. His words were drowned by the sound of flying feet. A crowd of men and boys were hurrying past, shouting as they ran.

Thorne dashed down to the gate, with Monty close behind him. "What is it?" he asked a man in the crowd.

"Ain't you heard? Chicago's burnin' up. They're gettin' all about it on the telegraph down at the depot!" He loped off after the others.

Thorne waited only long enough to pass the news to the group on the porch. "Not—not the South Side?" Mrs. Cobb asked through stiff lips. The Thorne home was far south, on the lake shore.

"I don't know. We're going down to the depot. No, you women mustn't come; you'll be crushed in the mob. I'll be back as soon as I get some news. You stay here, Mother Cobb—Elizabeth—and say a prayer, won't you, for Ellen and the baby?"

Mr. Cobb was already on his feet. Joining young Ward at the gate, the three men hurried off to the station.

The little building was jammed with an excited crowd. The young operator bent over the chattering telegraph key. Every minute he shouted fresh details as they came in on the wire. The crowd swelled, overflowing the platform and yard. And still the hoarse young voice went on with the tale of disaster, destruction, and death.

Monty, wedged in the crowd, listened with his hand on Bob Thorne's shoulder. The stone post office was gone and the "fireproof" *Tribune* building. The water supply had failed, leaving the firemen helpless. The flames had leaped the north branch of the river, setting the Gold Coast mansions ablaze.

Robert Thorne could not endure the suspense. He clutched the man nearest him, who had been an early arrival. "The South Side—what about the South Side? Did he say?"

"They're all right out there. It started west of the business district, and the wind's carrying it north."

Robert Thorne muttered a heartfelt prayer of his own. He knew that he ought to hurry with the good news to his wife's mother, but he could not tear himself away from the fearful story as it unrolled.

The loss of life could only be guessed at. Terrified throngs were pouring into the safety of Lincoln Park, dragging their pitiful possessions with them. The flames raged on unchecked. The fortress-built armory was a pile of crumbled rubble. The city gasworks blew up with a roar like thunder. On the whole of the near North Side, only the granite Water Tower still stood. Not a building remained on Clark Street, Wells Street, Rush Street—the names ran together as the operator's weary voice called them off.

"Rush Street?" Bob Thorne gasped. "Monty, isn't that where—"

"Yes." Monty could say no more.

The date was October 8, 1871—a date that lives in history as the day of the great Chicago fire.

It brought suffering and death and loss to thousands. What Montgomery Ward lost was a small thing by comparison. But the livery stable where he had stored his stock was on Rush Street. A stable hand perished there and twenty horses. Valuable carriages and wagons were destroyed. And the flames did not halt for a forlorn little hoard of calico, paper collars, and winter underwear.

10

MONTY'S LUCK TURNS

Every cent of Ward's savings had gone into the burned merchandise. There was nothing for it but to start all over again. He moved to a cheaper boardinghouse and cut his living expenses to the bone. And he thanked his stars that he had had sense enough to hang onto his job with Partridge Brothers.

The firm kept him busy. The fire had totally destroyed Chicago's central business district. With undaunted courage, the city was rebuilding on the ruins. The retailers, housed in temporary buildings, were scrambling for new goods to sell. The wholesale houses worked night and day to keep up with the demand. Monty had no time to brood over his ruined hopes.

He was not one to brood, in any case. This was just as well, for a new problem had arisen, one which had nothing to do with the fire.

The disaster left him with no stock to fill orders. But as the weeks went by, he had to face the bitter fact that there were no orders to fill.

Not a single answer came to the price lists he had sent out. If his merchandise had not gone up in flames, it would still be lying untouched in the livery-stable loft. No one wanted the bargains he had assembled with such anxious care.

For this, he saw now, he had only himself to blame. He had made up his mailing list at random, from farmers' names collected on his travels. These people did not know him or have any reason to trust him. They did not feel like sending off good money to a stranger for merchandise they had not seen. If he were to start again with any hope of success, he must find some way to win their confidence.

This was a knotty problem, and it gave him some sleepless nights. He was still struggling with it when the solution came by sheer good luck.

Ellen Thorne had asked him to Sunday dinner at the Thorne home. Her other guest was her Uncle Jerome of Kalamazoo. Uncle Jerome was in Chicago on business— very important business to him, and something he enjoyed talking about. It was from Jerome Cobb that Ward first learned of the Order of Patrons of Husbandry— or, to call it by its familiar name, the National Grange.

The Grange was a fraternal order of farmers devoted to advancing farmers' interests by united action. It was only a few years old, but already something like twenty thousand Grange lodges had been organized across the nation. Illinois had a strong Grange branch. Mr. Cobb was interested in organizing one in Michigan.

77

Bob Thorne looked doubtful as Uncle Jerome reeled off the figures.

"If they're state organizations, where do you get your twenty thousand?" he asked. "There weren't that many states in the Union the last time I counted the stars in the flag."

Mr. Cobb laughed. "I forget that everybody doesn't know as much about it as I do, Bob. The state Granges are made up of local Granges. In any community where the farmers want to get together, they organize their own Grange. There are dozens of them in some states. But they all report to their state Grange, and there's a Master for each state. And the states report to a national Master—the same way the Masons do, or the Odd Fellows. The Grange is a lodge, organized just as all lodges are."

"With secret initiations, and passwords, and everything?" Mrs. Thorne asked. "I must say, as a lodge member's wife, we women get a little annoyed at all those secrets that only our husbands can know."

"Then you'd like the Grange, Ellen," her uncle answered. "Yes, it has its secret ritual, like other lodges. But there's this difference. Women are accepted as full members. The Grange figures that what it is doing is as important to the farmers' wives as it is to the farmers themselves. Their help is needed, and they come in on the same footing as the men."

Montgomery Ward had listened in silence, but with quickening interest. Now he put in a quiet word.

"Just what *is* the Grange doing for the farmers, Mr. Cobb? I'd like to know."

Uncle Jerome was happy to tell him. The movement was only getting under way. Not nearly enough had been done yet. But the future was rosy with promise. Acting together, the farmers could demand fair market prices, lower railroad rates for shipping their crops, better rural schools, and improved roads. One farmer alone could do nothing about these things. But "In union there is strength," Mr. Cobb quoted.

"I can't begin to tell you all the ways the Grange can help the farmer," he went on earnestly. "Here in Illinois, they're talking about saving on what they have to pay for farm implements. They figure if they can put their orders together, they can buy at wholesale and cut out the middleman's profit. Maybe you city fellows don't know what that means to farmers."

"And maybe we do," Bob Thorne cut in excitedly. "Uncle, my friend Ward here has been up to his neck in a scheme to do exactly what you're talking about—to help the farmers save by cutting out the middleman's profit. I think you ought to know about it. I think the Grange ought to know."

"If it's for the good of the Grange, I'll be glad to hear it," the older man answered. "Go ahead, Mr. Ward."

Monty needed no further encouragement. Eagerly he

poured it all out. This was the opportunity he had been groping for—a way to win the farmers' trust. What better way could there be? If their own Grange vouched for him, the members could not doubt his honesty.

"I couldn't run to big things like farm implements," he admitted. "But farmers have to buy little things, too. Say I could get Grange support. Say they'd make me their official drygoods supply house. I could save them money, Mr. Cobb—don't you see I could? And they'd be sure of getting good value for their money. I— Well, what do you think?"

"I think the Grange people ought to know about it," Mr. Cobb answered. "I can't speak for them. I guess, from the way I've been talking, you'd think I was high up in the lodge. Actually, I'm not even a member yet. That's what I'm here for—to see some of the Illinois officials and find out how to get a branch started around Kalamazoo. We don't have a state Grange in Michigan yet, but our people are anxious to get organized. So of course I'm in no position to say whether the Grange would get behind your scheme."

"But you do think it's worth calling to their attention?" Bob Thorne pressed.

"I certainly do. Now let's see. The Master of the Illinois Grange, Alonzo Golder, is coming in from down state this week. I have an appointment with him on Tuesday. When I get through with my business, I'll bring up yours, Ward. Then if he thinks well of it, you can go see him be-

fore he leaves. Better have all your facts and figures
ready. I understand Mr. Golder is a pretty shrewd businessman as well as a fine farmer."

"I'll be ready for him," Monty promised.

He scarcely tasted the rest of Ellen's good dinner. As
soon as he finished, he excused himself and hurried away.
"I want to look over my facts and figures," he explained.

Thorne walked to the gate with him. "Well, your
chance has come," he exulted. "Once you get the Grange
behind you, it'll be clear sailing."

"Except for one thing," Ward said soberly. "Money.
I haven't nearly enough yet to buy any sort of stock. If
Mr. Golder told me to go ahead tomorrow, I couldn't do
it."

Thorne hesitated. "Monty, the mail-order business is
your idea. But I believe in it as strongly as you do. I
think it's the biggest thing that's come along in our lifetime. I'd like to be in on it. Would you—well, would
you take me as a partner?"

"Would I? There's nothing I'd like better! Do you
really mean it, Bob?"

"I mean it all right. I couldn't put in much money,
though—a few hundreds at best. But we won't need as
much cash as you think. With Grange backing, we could
surely get some credit."

"I suppose so," Ward said doubtfully. "I'd rather keep
it on a cash footing if I can, because I can get better prices
that way. And the less I have to pay, the lower I can

make my own prices. Anyway, once the orders begin coming in, we'll have cash to operate with. Well, we'll work it out after we see what Mr. Golder says. If you're going to be a partner, you'll have to come with me when I talk to him. Between us, we ought to be able to persuade him."

The interview with Mr. Golder went very well. He asked searching questions and got honest answers. When the two young men left, he had promised to consult with his associates and let them know what the Grange decided.

Some anxious weeks went by before the answer came. In the course of those winter weeks, Elizabeth Cobb paid a long visit to her Chicago sister.

Ellen Thorne, a more indulgent chaperone than her mother, offered no obstacles to Monty's courtship. Knowing he had no money to spare, Elizabeth sweetly insisted that she did not care for theaters. Instead, they took long walks through the leafless parks and along the wind-swept lake shore.

It was on one of these strolls that he asked the important question and got the answer that made him the happiest man in the world.

"We won't tell Mama just yet," Elizabeth decided. "She likes you, Monty, and I think she'll be pleased. But she's sure to ask what your prospects are. And you don't know that yourself right now, do you? Wait till you hear from the Grange."

There could be no doubt now that Monty's luck had

turned for the better. The Grange answer, a favorable one, came in late March.

With the letter in his hand, he took the first train for Kalamazoo. Had Mrs. Cobb been ten times the dragon she was, he was prepared to win Elizabeth or perish. He was agreeably surprised to find that no battle was needed.

"You and Lizzie fixed it up, have you?" she asked mildly. "I thought there was something in the wind when she overstayed her time with Ellen. Well, I don't know where she could have done any better. You're a good boy, Monty, and a smart one. There are big things ahead for you—I always said so. Remember that my little girl deserves the best. I'm counting on you to see that she gets it."

The wedding took place in Kalamazoo one month later. It was a very quiet affair, with only the families present.

Elizabeth, gently but firmly refusing a big wedding, had also had her own way about gifts. She did not want a solid silver service and English bone china and imported table damask. It was generous of Uncle Jerome to offer to furnish her new home, but she would not have a home just yet. She and Monty were going to begin their new life in a modest boardinghouse. "I'd rather have the money instead," she told her family candidly.

The prosperous Cobbs responded with substantial checks. Added to Monty's savings and what Thorne could furnish, they came to $2,400.

It was on this capital that the multi-million-dollar house of Montgomery Ward and Company was founded. Six months after the Chicago fire, one month after Monty's marriage, the new firm opened its doors for business.

11

"CONSULT OUR CATALOGUE"

The first Montgomery Ward catalogue went out to Grange members in the spring of 1872. It was a single printed sheet, 8 x 12 inches, with no pictures and very little descriptive matter.

The original price list, which perished in the fire, had contained nothing but drygoods items. Ward had not forgotten how miserably it had failed to impress the farmers. It might be that not distrust alone held back their orders. Possibly the merchandise itself had not been what they wanted. This time, at least he would try for greater variety. What did a farm family need, he asked his wife, that could not be bought to good advantage in the village store?

"Presents," Elizabeth answered thoughtfully. "Christmas and birthdays and weddings come on the farm the same as everywhere else. Farmers don't buy just bare necessities all the time, any more than town people do. There are occasions when they want something nice, something extra to give as a gift. And I don't know where they'd get it. Even in Kalamazoo, there's only one jewelry store. I don't believe there are any in the smaller towns. Where can a young farmer buy a bracelet for his girl's birthday? Or maybe a fan, or a parasol? Or—"

"Wait, wait!" Ward was scribbling furiously. "Jewelry—table silver, now. Why didn't I think of that? And what else did you say? Fans, parasols—" He pushed the paper across to her. "You make me a list, my dear. You know about these things. Put down everything you think they'd like, and I'll hunt around until I find them at a fair price."

Elizabeth's help was invaluable, especially in choosing items that would appeal to women. She knew fashions, and she saw to it that her husband's choices followed the current styles.

"*Not* merino dress goods," she said firmly. "Nobody's wearing merino this year. And anyway, that's a winter fabric. They're doing spring sewing now. What they'll want is light summer silk or mull for Sunday, and calico and gingham for every day. Don't forget lace to trim the dress-up ones, too."

"What kind of lace?" he inquired. "Or does it make any difference?"

His wife gave him a kindly smile. "It makes a lot of difference, Monty. I think you'd better take me along when you go to buy women's things."

He accepted her offer with gratitude. It was thanks to Elizabeth's unerring good taste that the farm women were offered a choice of merchandise as up-to-date as they could have found at Marshall Field's.

That first catalogue sheet listed 163 articles. The most expensive of them was a lady's gold-plated watch at $8.00. Nothing was priced below $1.00, but that sum would buy 10 yards Heavy Indian Head sheeting, or 5 boxes Paper Collars and 1 brace Suspenders, or 12 New-Style Ruches for the Neck. Here are some of the other bargains:

1 Hoop Skirt, 1 Bustle, and 1 Hair Braid	$1.00
12 Yards Japanese Striped Silk Poplin	1.25
5 Yards Valenciennes Lace	1.00
2 Pair Men's Cassimere Pants	3.00
8 Pair Child's Balmoral Stockings	1.00
10 Yards Lancaster Gingham	1.00
1 Lady's Set, Pin and Earrings, Fine Onyx, Set in Gold	3.00
6 Heavy Extra Plated Silver Napkin Rings	1.50
6 Fine Combs, 6 Coarse Combs, 1 Hairbrush, and 5 Papers English Pins	1.00
1 Stereoscope with 6 Views, Walnut Frame, Good Glass	1.00
1 Plain Gold Wedding Ring, All Sizes	2.00

The first mailing list was made up of Grange members, the names supplied by the Iowa and Illinois lodges. There is no record of who sent in the first order, or for what.

But the first order came, and then the next. It began as a tiny trickle, and it ended in a flood that nearly washed the new firm off its feet.

The partners had rented a room in a new building on Clark Street, erected since the fire. It was on the top floor, and only fourteen feet long and twelve feet wide. A single desk was squeezed in among the boxes of stock, piled to the ceiling. The only employee was a teen-age boy to wrap packages and carry them to the post office.

The boy had the place to himself for the first few weeks, except when Ward or Thorne dropped in after their own working hours. They had rented a post-office box, and one of the partners always stopped by to pick up the mail. The first hint of success came when the post-office clerk called Ward back.

"Here's some more letters I couldn't cram in. Reckon you'll have to rent a bigger box, Mr. Ward. You better see the postmaster about it, if you don't want your mail to get lost back here."

Every one of the incoming letters contained cash or money orders. With the money as it came in, Monty scurried around town buying new stock to replace what had moved out. It was no longer possible to wait for the manufacturer to offer him job lots. He needed bigger quantities now, and he needed them at once. He bought from the manufacturer when he could, from the whole-saler when he must. But always he kept his own profit to the fixed 5 per cent or 10 per cent, and always he made certain that he was getting only high-grade merchandise.

His activities in his own business conflicted seriously with his duties for Partridge Brothers. The day soon came when he handed in his resignation and settled down to full-time employment as the Montgomery Ward company's senior partner.

Even in his St. Joe days, he had had a passion for system and order. As his first bewilderment passed, he organized the new business along orderly lines. This was not easy. He was a pioneer in his field, with no rules to go by. He worked out his own rules by applying sound common sense.

As he saw it, his first duty was to his customers. Now that he could place orders of respectable size, the suppliers were anxious for his trade. But did the farmers want what he had to offer? What *did* the farmers want? He was anxious to meet their needs and wishes. The best way to find out, he thought, was to ask them.

The customers grew used to having a friendly handwritten letter come along with their orders. Ward admitted that he could not carry in stock everything his customers might need. If there was something else, something not on his list, he would be glad to buy it and send it along at 5 per cent over what it cost him.

When these special requests came in, he studied them with great care. It might be that only one farmer in the world wanted a sidesaddle for a Shetland pony. He bought and shipped the tiny saddle, but he did not add that article to his catalogue.

What he did find was that there was a strong demand for sewing machines. These were high-priced at best. With the wholesale and retail profit added in, many a farmer's wife shook her head and continued to sew by hand. It was a proud day for Ward when he concluded a deal with a sewing-machine manufacturer. It enabled him to offer the article at $30.00, a good twenty dollars under the retail price.

Besides studying his customers' wants, Ward had the office details to attend to. At first it was all very simple. He and Elizabeth had moved to a small house on Ohio

Street. The firm now owned a light wagon and a horse. Every morning the boy drove to the post office and collected the mail. He stopped at the Ward house for breakfast, and then drove his employer to work. For the rest of the day, he and Ward packed shipments. In late afternoon, the boy loaded his wagon and hauled the packages to the post office.

The firm outgrew the wagon as it outgrew the office space. Sewing machines, farm tools, harness, and baby carriages, as they were added, required room for storage. These heavy articles had to be shipped by railroad express or freight. To get them to the station, a stout dray and a team of draft horses was needed—and another dray, and then another. Needed also was a good-sized warehouse and office.

The firm had made several moves by 1874, each time to larger quarters. In that year, Robert Thorne gave up his lumber business and came to join his partner. Their single-page catalogue had grown to a twenty-four-page booklet. The 1875 one had seventy-two pages and the first pictures of articles to be sold.

Three years later, in 1878, the catalogue offered a ready-made woman's dress. This created a sensation. Ready-to-wear garments had long been confined to men's suits and overcoats and women's coats. A few manufacturers were beginning to experiment with dresses for women. They sold to the big city stores: Macy's and Wanamaker's in New York, Marshall Field's in Chicago.

In the smaller towns and on the farms, home sewing continued to be the rule. The novelty of buying a dress complete, ready to put on, was something the Grange ladies had never expected. They sent in their orders, and they showed off their new frocks at church. Women who were not Grange members were impressed enough to write in for catalogues.

For the first few years, the Ward Company served Grange families only. The catalogues identified it as "The Original Grange Supply House." But as more and more requests came in from outsiders, Ward consulted with Grange officials. With their full approval, he opened his field to the general public. The relationship between the firm he founded and the Grange organization remained a warm and friendly one, and remains so to this day. The National Grange is still a powerful force working for the good of farmers. And the Montgomery Ward catalogue still has an honored place in Grange homes.

The friendship between Ward and the Grange was cemented by some hard-won battles, fought side by side. The Grange had its enemies among the railroads and the produce buyers who had victimized the farmers before they organized for their own protection. Ward's enterprise, which helped the Grange, did not endear him to these interests. In addition, the mail-order business had some bitter foes of its own.

Chief among them, of course, were the small-town stores, which had prospered on the farm trade. Local merchants put on some vicious campaigns, supported by their local newspapers.

In several country towns, catalogue burnings were held in the public squares. Some merchants offered as much as 50 cents apiece for every catalogue brought in to be burned. The canny farmers sent for new ones, sold their old ones, and spent the merchant's money on orders to Montgomery Ward.

Ward met these attacks with serene good nature. He believed wholeheartedly that he was rendering a service to the farmers, a service which the local stores had failed to render. No farmer was compelled to buy from his catalogue. If a farmer chose to shop in the nearest town, that was his right. It was equally his right to shop by mail. Ward was quite willing to leave the farmers to their free choice.

As the years went by, it became clear that there was room for both systems. The merchants' dark fears that the mail-order scheme would put them out of business were not realized. What did happen was that the town stores improved, both in quality and variety of stock offered, and in fairer prices. Ward competition put the ax to the old "anything is good enough for farmers" theory. And the storekeepers found, to their surprise, that the farm market was worth cultivating.

This happy result did not come about overnight. The early years were years of bitter hostility from retail merchants. The hostility was at its height when, in 1886,

Ward's first competitor in his own line entered the field.

The mail-order firm of Sears, Roebuck and Company began by selling watches and jewelry only. In a few years it added general merchandise and put out a catalogue very similar to Ward's. Like him, Richard Sears catered to the farm trade and also offered a money-back guarantee.

Rivals though they were, the two mail-order houses had better judgment than to fight each other. They had their hands full with fighting the small-town merchants who were determined to ruin them both.

Once that danger was safely past, Ward and Sears, Roebuck settled down to a healthy competition between catalogues. Each had to add variety and trim its prices in the effort to outdo the other. The customers benefited by this competition, and it cannot be said that either mail-order house suffered. Side by side, they have expanded into two giant corporations whose very names stand for all that is best in American business life.

12

THE BEST FOR ELIZABETH

"My little girl deserves the best," Mother Cobb had told Monty. "I'm counting on you to see that she gets it."

"The best," by the old lady's small-town standards, meant a comfortable home, a maid to do the housework, and some pretty clothes. These things Montgomery Ward was able to give his wife by the close of the 1880's.

He gave them proudly and gladly. Elizabeth had made an ideal poor man's wife, thrifty and capable. His success was largely due to her unfailing confidence and encouragement. Now the time had come when he could do something to repay her. It seemed that he could never do enough.

He surprised her on her birthday by the gift of a handsome new home near Lincoln Park. The first dinner party given there was a family one, attended only by the Thornes.

The two families were very close. The Thornes had five boys and a girl; the Wards, one daughter. Marjorie Ward was a fairy child, graceful and delicate, so frail that her health was a constant anxiety. Because of this, she was being tutored at home until she should be old enough for an Eastern finishing school.

Mrs. Thorne and her younger children arrived in the late afternoon. Ward and Thorne would come together when the office closed. Marjorie took her cousins upstairs to see her new room, and Mrs. Thorne followed her sister into the dining room. She exclaimed in delight over the flower-laden table, set with new silver and china.

"It's beautiful! Too pretty to be wasted on just the family. You'll have to begin doing some real entertaining, Sis, now that you have this big house."

"That's what Monty says," Mrs. Ward answered. "It's funny. He's so shy and retiring himself, but he wants to see me in society. As if I cared anything about that!"

"Well, you'll have to care, for his sake," her sister said. "It's one of the things he can give you, and he wants to give you everything. Bob's just the same. They'd be disappointed if we wanted to keep on living the same old way. Our husbands are rich men now, Sis. We have to learn to be rich men's wives."

"Rich!" Elizabeth Ward said wonderingly. "It's still hard to believe."

"Not for me," her sister said cheerfully. "And don't pretend you aren't pleased about it, my dear. *I* am. I never had it so hard as you did, because there was the lumber business to depend on. But even so, I did plenty of penny-pinching when the children were little. I'm thankful that those days are behind me."

"Well, I am, too. Of course I am. It's just that I— Well, it's hard to think of myself as a rich woman."

"It'll get easier, once you're used to it," Ellen Thorne answered briskly. "For my part, I mean to enjoy every minute of it. Our husbands earned their money honestly. We helped them all we could. We tried to be good poor men's wives. I don't see why we can't be good rich men's wives, now that— Oh, Bob, you startled me!"

She broke off as her husband came quietly into the room. He kissed his wife and turned to Elizabeth.

"Monty will be a little late, but in plenty of time for dinner. He had a last-minute caller, so he told me to come on ahead."

"Oh? Let's go into the parlor, then. Or you two go— I want to speak to the cook."

She turned toward the kitchen, and the Thornes settled themselves in the plush-and-walnut parlor. Elizabeth joined them a minute later.

"Monty promised me he wouldn't be late," she remarked. "But I suppose some business affair came up at the last minute."

"It wasn't business exactly," Thorne explained. "A worker from the Home Missions came to see him. She had a story of a poor West Side family practically freezing to death for want of coal. I'd have given her a couple of dollars and got rid of her, but you know how soft-hearted Monty is. He wanted to know all about what the

Missions do. She was more than willing to tell him. She had a satchel full of hard-luck cases."

Elizabeth's sweet face grew serious. "I remember one winter when we had a hard time keeping warm ourselves. I hope Monty gave them all the coal they need. But of course he would!"

A little later Ward came in, stamping the snow from his feet. Elizabeth summoned the young people, and the family moved into the dining room. After the plates were served, Mrs. Ward turned to her husband.

"Dear, you did give that poor family some coal, didn't you?"

"Which family?" He smiled at her. "There's more than one cold heating stove on the West Side, my dear. If you could have heard some of the stories that woman told me! It wound up with my giving her an order for six hundred tons, to be charged to me. I hope you approve."

"Oh, I do, I do!" Elizabeth answered. "I'd just been telling Ellen that it was hard to get used to being rich. But I wasn't thinking then— Why, we can do so much good with our money! We know what it's like to be poor. There was that time we couldn't pay the doctor's bill, remember? Were there any sick people in the families she told you about?"

"She didn't say," Ward answered. "All she had on her mind today was coal—this has been a hard winter, you know. I told her to distribute the six hundred tons as she thought best, but to keep my name out of it. Just say it came from the Missions. I don't want people to think I'm showing off."

Bob Thorne laughed. "No one will ever accuse you of showing off, old man. I'll bet even Elizabeth doesn't know of some of the folks you've helped through the years—and sometimes when you hadn't a dime to spare, either. Now that you can go in for charity on a large scale, you'll have to quit hiding your light under a bushel. People expect successful men to become benefactors."

Montgomery Ward looked panic-stricken. "I'll never be a benefactor!" he declared. "I mean— Well, of course I'll give where it's needed. But I won't be thanked for it. I won't have my name in the papers. I just won't! It would make me feel like a perfect fool!"

He spoke from the depths of his heart. Never, so long as he lived, did Montgomery Ward permit his name to be used in connection with any public charity. He continued to give out of his growing fortune as he had given in his early days, generously, but in secret, shrinking from any show of gratitude. No one will ever know how many hospital beds he endowed under assumed names. No one will ever know how many tons of coal and bushels of groceries went to poor families from an unknown friend.

His wife and daughter fell in with his wishes. It was not until after his death that Mrs. Ward and Marjorie openly undertook the series of philanthropies that make their names so beloved in the Middle West.

The size of their gifts made continued secrecy impossible. Northwestern University, for instance, could scarcely receive its $8,000,000 Medical Center from a secret giver. Mrs. Ward gave it, and saw the cornerstone laid. Completed after her death, it stands as a memorial to her husband.

The Thorne fortune, too, would endow munificent charities. But on that winter evening in the new house, multi-million-dollar gifts were as yet undreamed of. Only the first million was in sight, though many more were to come. It would not be long, however, before the two sisters moved with gracious ease into leadership of Chicago society. The Thorne boys, entering the family firm later, became successful businessmen in their own right.

Charles Thorne, the eldest, was already a Montgomery Ward employee at the time of the dinner party. He was not present, for he had been sent to see a furniture manufacturer in Grand Rapids. But he surprised them all by appearing just as the Thorne carriage was being brought around late that night.

"I couldn't wait to tell you, Dad—Uncle Monty," he said breathlessly. "If we order enough of them, they'll come down 20 per cent on those bedroom suites. I know you said to try for 10 per cent, but I thought I could do better if I was firm about it. I talked right up to them. Said they'd meet our figure or we'd go elsewhere. And they gave in," he ended with pride.

The two older men exchanged glances. It was little more than a year since young Charlie had left college to

come into the business. He had started at the bottom as a stock clerk, working his way up through all the departments. He had done well in all of them. And on this, his first buying mission, he had done better than they could have hoped.

"It looks to me," his father said gravely, "as if you'll be a vice-president one of these days. What do you think, Monty?"

Ward laid a friendly hand on his nephew's shoulder. "And a vice-president who's earned his job, not gotten it by family favor. You're all right, Charlie. If your brothers turn out as well, you boys will be running the company by the time Bob and I are ready to retire."

13

THE WATCHDOG
OF THE WATER FRONT

It was a bright summer morning in 1893, the year of Chicago's great Columbian Exposition. Montgomery Ward left his desk for a minute to look down on the busy sidewalk below his office window.

This international World's Fair had brought hordes of visitors to Chicago, many of them from foreign lands. Here and there the watcher could pick out the red fez of a Turk, or an Arab in his desert robes. But mostly the crowd was made up of American sight-seers from the neighboring states. A good many of them were Ward customers. It pleased Mr. Ward now to see that a fair number of the strollers turned in at his street door.

The seven-story Montgomery Ward building, which had been completed in 1890, was the showplace of Michigan Avenue. Besides its height, it was celebrated for its six steam elevators and the magnificence of its marble lobby. There was nothing to sell, but a great deal to see, within its walls. And sight-seers were warmly welcomed. If they liked, they could join a free guided tour of the warehouse, with its assortment of twenty-five thousand items, or the mail room, where thirty clerks did nothing all day long but open letters.

Even better, to footsore Exposition visitors, was the Customers' Parlor. This was a vast room, comfortably furnished with rocking chairs and sofas, with a washroom and a row of writing desks.

Many a weary farm wife let her family go on to the Fair without her, and spent a restful afternoon rocking and resting in the Ward Parlor. For reading matter, there was a plentiful supply of new catalogues. If something struck her fancy, the writing desk was handy to make out her order now and save a stamp. But there was no pressure to order anything. The Parlor was a free offering of neighborly hospitality to Ward customers. It paid off in such an immense amount of good will that it was retained after the Exposition closed.

Ward's window-gazing was interrupted by his secretary.

"It's that Mr. Small, the reporter from the *Tribune*," he explained. "I've told him before that you don't give out interviews and you don't want to be written up in their 'Millionaires of Chicago' series. But he says it's something else this time. His editor sent him to find out how the water-front fight is going. Will you see him, sir?"

Ward frowned. "If it's about that—yes, I suppose I'd better. Send him in."

The young reporter entered with some hesitation. It

was well known that Montgomery Ward disliked personal publicity. This was not the first time Fred Small had sought an interview. He had never reached the inner office before. Now that he was here, he must make the most of it.

Mentally he was taking note of the office and the man. A big room with wide plate-glass windows overlooking the avenue, richly but soberly furnished in mahogany and brown leather, with a plain brown carpet. The man himself—tall, slim, square-shouldered, with thick brown hair and well-tended mustache. Young looking for his fifty years. Carefully dressed in black broadcloth and stiff-bosomed shirt, with a white carnation in his buttonhole.

"Mr. Small, I believe?" It was a pleasant voice, although it sounded a little impatient now. "You told my secretary you wanted to see me about the water-front fight. I don't know why. Your paper must know that there's nothing new there. We've taken another appeal, and it's still pending."

"Yes, sir," the reporter said eagerly. "This isn't a news story. It's a feature article for the Sunday edition. A lot of people don't know what your suit is all about. My editor wants me to tell the whole story from the beginning. How you came to start the fight in the first place. Why you object to a firehouse and an armory, and—"

"Who said I objected to a firehouse and an armory?" Ward interrupted. "Where do you get that impression?"

"Why—I guess it's because you're suing the city to

make them tear down the firehouse and to keep them from building the armory. It certainly looks as if you objected to them, sir."

"I have no objection in the world to a firehouse and an armory," Ward said with decision. "They are useful structures, and we must have them. I do object to having them in that particular spot. Come here, young man."

He crossed to the window and beckoned the reporter to stand beside him.

"Here's our side of Michigan Avenue, lined with handsome, dignified stores and office buildings, among the finest in the country. Now look across the street to the other side, and beyond. What do you see? The lake shore? Oh, no. The lake is there, but you can't see it. Take a good look, Mr. Small. Tell me what you do see."

What he saw was a squalid collection of livery stables and squatters' shacks, and a mountain of tin cans and ashes. The only respectable building was a two-story wooden firehouse.

"It's not a pretty sight," the reporter admitted. "But the shacks and the dump heap will go when the city gets around to carrying out its plans. After the armory there'll be a new post office, and a central police station, and maybe a museum, if Mr. Field decides to give us one. Unless you succeed in stopping any building at all, that is. Some people say you're standing in the way of progress, Mr. Ward."

Montgomery Ward sighed. "I know they do. Come and sit down, my boy. I want you to get this straight."

He waited until Small was settled in a chair beside his desk. Then he went on with deep earnestness.

"I don't believe there's a man in Chicago who cares more about the city's progress than I do. I saw the great fire. I saw what Chicago did to build a greater city out of the ruins. I'm proud of my city. It's going to be the biggest city in the world one day. It can be the most beautiful one, if we just have the vision to make it so. Vision, Mr. Small; that's what it takes. You've seen what's outside that window now. Do you know what I'd like to see instead?"

He did not wait for a reply.

"Not an armory, not a museum, not any structure built by man. Instead, the blue waters of Lake Michigan, the blue sky, the sweep of sandy shore. Between us and the beach, green grass and flowers, shade trees and benches and walks. A place where store and office workers can rest their tired eyes and refresh their spirits in the noon hour. Yes, a park, Mr. Small. A park right here, in the business heart of the city, where no one would expect a park to be. And where it's needed most! Well——" He broke off with a smile.

"That's the lake front as I see it, Mr. Small. The land is the property of the city of Chicago. The city government has the obligation to use it for the best interests of all the citizens. I'm a citizen, and I do not think our best interests would be served by cluttering it with buildings that can well be located elsewhere. Your paper doesn't agree with me. Very few people do agree. It's been three years since I brought my first suit, and there's a hard fight yet to come. But if it takes the rest of my life and every cent I have, I'm going to save our water front in its God-given beauty. You can call that standing in the way of progress if you like. It's where I stand."

"I wish I could stand beside you, sir," the young reporter said, with awe in his voice. "But——well, my paper is against your suit, as I guess you know. A lot of the big businessmen are. They can't see progress in anything but building. All I can do is put down what you say. The

Tribune is fair, you know. They're not on your side, but they'll let me give your side just as you've given it to me."

"That's all I ask," Ward told him. "My fellow citizens may not appreciate what I'm trying to do for them now, but some day they will—or their children will. That's good enough for me."

Small brought out his notebook. "I don't have to write down what you've said about your reasons, Mr. Ward. It's something I'll never forget. But now let's be sure I have the legal part right. It was back in 1890 that you first sued to make the city clear the land, wasn't it? And to restrain them from building there? Yes, I've got that. Your petition was refused, and you carried it to a higher court. And now—"

Ward helped him fill in the details. Small's article, when it appeared, was an eloquent one which won some sympathy for the project. He headed it, "Montgomery Ward, Watchdog of the Water Front."

The title was fairly earned. At his own expense, Ward fought his battle doggedly through court after court. It took four court trials and long weary years of waiting before the battle was won. But won it was. The park is there, green and lovely against the blue lake, just as Ward saw it in his mind's eye.

Grant Park. Named for General Grant, who never saw it. It might better have borne the name of Montgomery Ward. For without him, no one would ever have seen it.

14

THE TWILIGHT YEARS

Ward's long water-front fight did not distract him from his company's business. Steadily the firm grew and expanded, adding new lines to the catalogue, new customers to the books. By the time the water-front fight ended, Montgomery Ward and Company was so huge that it needed five vice-presidents to head the various departments.

"You'll be a vice-president some day," Charlie Thorne's father had told his son. And Uncle Monty had predicted that one day the Thorne boys would be running the business.

They were all vice-presidents now, joining the company fresh from college and working their way up as the oldest brother had done. All of them delighted the older men by their quick grasp of problems and their willingness to follow the policies that had proved so effective. If they were not yet running the company, it was only because their father and uncle still kept the reins in their own hands.

Their wives were urging retirement. The firm was soundly established now, its worst difficulties behind it.

New difficulties would arise, but the young men they had trained were fully able to cope with them. Why not leave them to it and take a little ease and comfort?

The argument was a sound one. Montgomery Ward and Company was a huge corporation for those days. The original partners would not live to see the opening of the six hundred retail stores or the years of billion-dollar net sales. But it was a big company, the biggest in its field, a successful venture of which its founders could be proud. With assured success, much of the excitement of the early days was gone. Without too much regret, Ward and Thorne yielded to their wives' entreaties and withdrew from active management. This came in the early 1900's.

Robert Thorne celebrated his new freedom by taking his wife for a protracted trip around the world. Ward and Elizabeth accompanied them as far as Paris and then turned back. Marjorie was leaving school for the summer vacation, and they wanted to be home to welcome her.

Some years before, Ward had bought a summer place at Oconomowoc, Wisconsin, so that their delicate daughter might have country air. Marjorie loved the place. Her father had been able to spend only week ends there. Now they settled down for the summer.

Ward's parents came often to Oconomowoc, and their visits were returned. The old gentleman, retired from storekeeping, lived with his wife in the Niles home their son had built for them. The sisters were married and scattered to distant parts, but they, too, came home for family reunions. There were weeks when the Oconomowoc house overflowed with Wards and Thornes and Cobbs, with Grandmother Cobb keeping a sharp eye on the manners of the small fry.

Ward, who had always liked farmers, tried his hand at farming the estate. He was a gentleman farmer, he admitted, with hired men to do the work, and no need to show a profit. But he took a keen interest in his blue-ribbon dairy herd and in the fast trotters he bred. It was the first time in his life that he had had any real leisure, and he enjoyed it with boyish zest.

At first, the family spent their winters in their new home at Highland Park near Chicago. But one snowy December they went to California and fell in love with the mild climate of Pasadena. They bought a house there. Ward played golf at the country club and startled his neighbors by driving the first Stanley Steamer they had ever seen.

And so the tranquil, twilight years went by. They were happy years. Marjorie, as she grew up, shook off the frail health of her childhood days. She was her father's cherished companion, and her mother's efficient aide in charitable work. Moving from Chicago to Pasadena to Wisconsin in season, the Wards were never without warm friends and good neighbors. And always, of course, there were the Thornes, bound by lifelong ties that were never broken.

Twilight, happy years. The Wards were a long-lived

family. Montgomery Ward, always in rugged health, counted on many such years ahead. They ended for him on a bleak December day in 1913.

He had had a bad fall at Pasadena a few months before and suffered a broken hip. When it did not seem to heal properly, Mrs. Ward brought him back to Chicago for medical attention.

They arrived in the midst of a Chicago blizzard and took the long cold drive to Highland Park in a touring car. Ward remarked to his wife that night that he was afraid he had caught cold. He woke next morning in a raging fever, which the doctor pronounced pneumonia.

The end came a few days later. Montgomery Ward died on December 7, 1913, in his seventieth year.

There is a handsome monument over his grave in Chicago's Rose Hill cemetery, and the Medical Center stands as an additional memorial. His name would live on without them. It lives in every Montgomery Ward catalogue pouring from the press, and on the lips of families who say with perfect assurance, "You can't go wrong when you deal with Montgomery Ward."

1840/185